JAPANESE AIRCRAFT INDUSTRY

in WWII

USAF Report of 1946

Kawasaki Ki-61 "Hien"

*This book is based on a USAF Report
for 1946 and has been completely amended
with numerous additions*

ISBN 0-9469 9560 5

Galago Books 42 palace Grove, Bromley, Kent BR1 3HB, England

No part of this publication may be reproduced, stored in a retrieval system, or transmitted in any form or by any means, electronic, mechanical, photocopying, recording or other, without the prior permission in writing of the publishers

Previously published by ISO Publications in 1996

CONTENTS

1. INTRODUCTION

For years the Japanese have been branded as "copyists". Did this trait contribute to the defeat of the nation? Do such procedures indicate a lack of initiative on the part of the Japanese engineer?

It is true that the Japanese technical establishment leaned to a great degree upon the corresponding fields in Europe and America. This practice, however, especially in the field of military science, is more or less universal, and the great saving in time, expense and manpower warrants such action. An examination of weapons throughout history will show international use of the same basic designs. The famous U.S. Spingfield M 1903 rifle, manufactured and used extensively during both World Wars, was based on the design of the German Mauser. The highly efficient, though under exploited, Butterfly Bomb was copied and recently manufactured without deviation from the German model, by the U.S. Army Ordnance Department. Despite their great reliance upon imitations and their lagging technical level, the Japanese must be given credit for individual initiative, as is frequently evidenced not only by original designs but by their practice of materially improving copies. In suicide weapons, for example, Japanese originality is plainly evident. Many weapons, including our own Browning machine gun, were improved by the Japanese before final adoption.

The cast gains accrued through copying were to a degree offset by the difficulties encountered in mass-producing highly specialised items. Satisfactory fabrication of the Norden bombsight, for example, was greatly impeded through inefficient Japanese mass-productive methods.

Japan's technological level lagged behind that of the United States in much the same degree as the United States' lagged behind Germany. The Nipponese lag was due to it's late and incomplete industrial revolution which was hampered by the retention of many primitive methods in the less populated areas. The United States lag was primarily limited to the field of military weapons, and may be attributed to a pre-war pacifist attitude which prohibited sufficient appropriations for education and research into armament engineering.

By far the most towering handicap to Japanese technical advance was the lack of standardisation. Due to insufficient coordination between the Army and Navy, and amplified by their low technical levels, the variety of equipment, from large aircraft to small instruments, was tremendous. As a consequence, the technicians, short as they were in quality and quantity had to be used in weak dispersed groups. This condition brought about the requirements of unnecessary efforts in many already overtaxed fields; design, production, modification, maintenance, supply, and even in training. The problems did not end there, but reacted continuously in combat by directly impeding operations. By tracing the development of the Browning machine gun from initial adoption to combat employment one may get an insight on the consequences of non standardisation

The Japanese Air Forces required a calibre .50 aircraft machine gun. Why not adapt the Browning which had already been fully tried and proved by both the Americans and the British? The Japs not only adopted the gun, but incorporated some improvements in design, as well as increasing the rate of fire. The Army and Navy each set their own staffs of designers on separate projects for this calibre .50 Browning machine gun. This was obviously duplicate effort, but there still remained the possibility of eventually combining ideas and production potentials. On the contrary, however, each service insisted on adhering to specific minor variations in design. The result was that each air force began manufacturing their own individual calibre .50 machine guns; both Browning actions, but not quite identical enough to allow interchangeability of either assemblies of separate components. This condition was further aggravated by each air arm adopting different cartridge design; two cartridges in the same category, but the navy adopted a calibre .51 cartridge in opposition to the Army's calibre .50.

Commander Kofukuda cites an instance in his combat experiences when his squadron had to stand down operations because the machine gun ammunition on a well-stocked adjacent Army air base would not fit the chamber of their similar guns. The story of the calibre .50 Browning is not an isolated case, but is typical of Japan's self-imposed handicaps resulting from poor cooperation. Later, despite long established opinions of American arms experts to the effect that the calibre .50 was the maximum possible size for the Browning type mechanism, Jap initiative produced and used operationally a Browning 20 millimetre machine gun and had completed an experimental 37 millimetre model.

Mitsubishi Ki-46-III (Dinah) Army Reconnaissance aircraft

Mitsubishi Ki-67 (Peggy) Army Reconnaissance aircraft

2. ARMY-NAVY

GENERAL
Throughout the war, numerous efforts were extended to amplify cooperation between the Army and Navy. It became increasingly evident that many operational difficulties could be traced back to nonstandardisation of equipment. Finally, a belated all-out attempt at "full" cooperation was made, even to the extent of designing and using common aircraft. However, continued rivalry and discord between the air forces seriously hampered even this final effort, as is evident in the development of jet and rocket-propelled aircraft.

STEPS TOWARD COOPERATION
Before the war, the joint Army and Navy Committee was created, and although this encouraged some cooperation and exchanges of technical knowledge in many fields not striking results were noted.

In 1942 the Army-Navy Committee was formed in view of the urgent necessity of expediting the solution of the increasing wartime problems. Efforts were generally limited to research, with negligible results.

Finally, in 1943, in answer to the ever-increasing burdens being imposed upon the manufacturers, and in view of the shortage of materials, it was realised that the most vital problem was the necessity for a certain degree of uniformity between Army and Navy equipment. The previously formed Air Committee was replaced by the Army-Navy Technical Committee established by the chiefs of the Army and Navy Air Headquarters. Proposals were studied for joint research, design, and production of weapons and equipment. There were a few specific joint achievements in the field of research, but due to persistent disagreement on ideas, full cooperation was never attained.

FACTORS HINDERING STANDARDISATION
Some high technical officials believed that unification in the early stages of research would take away the rival spirit and, thereby, reduce efficiency. This was possibly true in some fields of basic research, but the Army and Navy maintained one-sided opinions right through to the end of the production line.

Due to the late start towards cooperation in design, extensive joint use of weapons and equipment would have proved impractical. The already widespread operational use of individual designs prohibited standardisation without comprehensive re--equipment of units. Even standardisation of simple aircraft components was hampered by the following factors:

- The Army Air Force used a 24 volt electrical system since 1938. The "Navy did not switch to the 24 volt system until April 1945, and even then production was limited to two types of aircraft.
- Aircraft machine gun ammunition 'could not be used jointly due to differences in gun barrel chamber dimensions.
- Variations in the design of existing amounts precluded joint use" of most aerial weapons (guns, cannon and rocket launchers).

The late initiation of joint design and production on new models of equipment was far from the solution, as these new standard types represented but a small fraction of the total operational equipment. Any attempt at large scale re-equipment of units with standardised weapons would accrue disadvantages far outweighing the potential gains of joint production. Some of the factors involved would be:

- Major modifications of equipment and installations.
- Retooling of factories
- Immediate or gradual replacement of large existing stocks, further complicating the already complex supply problem.
- Retraining of personnel in operational maintenance.
- Revision of existing tactics.

REPERCUSSIONS IN THE COMBAT ZONE

In addition to numerous efforts of combat being nipped in the bud by non-standardisation of aircraft components and weapons, many sustained joint operations were seriously hindered.

Due to differences in cruising ranges of Army and Navy aircraft, co-ordinated operations, particularly in sea warfare, were relatively ineffective. An example is the futile attempt of the Army to provide satisfactory fighter cover for the naval special attack corps in the Okinawa campaign. Major differences in radio equipment design resulted in poor intercommunication between Army and Navy aircraft. Due to variance in design of IFF equipment, accurate identification of both Army and Navy aircraft was often impossible.

Direct lack of coordination was also evident in combat. During the Okinawa campaign nine flying regiments of Ki-67's were scheduled for torpedo operations. The Navy furnished the torpedoes but had no personnel to assist in their adjustment. As a result, only two of the regiments were able to go into combat, and the remaining units were later returned to normal bombing operations.

Kawasaki Ki-32 (Mary) Army light bomber

Yokosuka P1Y Ginga (Frances) Navy Medium Bomber

Kawasaki Ki-100 –II (Tony) Army Fighter

3. TECHNICAL AID FROM GERMANY

GENERAL

Outside aid to the pre-1941 Japanese war machine was not limited to German assistance. Quantities of aircraft instruments and components were purchased from other powers, including the United States. In Toyokawa arsenal, the Navy's most important aircraft gun and ammunition plant, there were installed equal numbers of both German and American machine tools.

Prior to and during the early period of the war, German assistance was generally limited to granting permission to the Japanese to purchase specimens of standard aircraft and equipment. The planes were generally used for study and experiment; but other items, such as instruments, were released in quantity for operational use.

The most active investigation of German aircraft materials and aeronautical data was launched during the period 1939 to 1941. Investigation teams were formed with Army and Navy personnel as heads and including civilian representatives. These groups visited key German factories, studied design and production techniques, and brought back specimens which were subject to intensive study. In addition, civilian technical representatives of firms like Mitsubishi received aeronautical data from military attaches. After Pearl Harbour, the dispatching .of such teams was necessarily halted, and such cooperation was thereafter generally limited to undetailed military cables.

Germany was reluctant to cope rate wholeheartedly with the Japanese. Despite early liaison, it was not until late in 1943 that concrete assistance was given and Japs finally permitted to enter the Luftwaffe's "Wright Field" at Braunschweig. Even then, much information was withheld, and Japanese admission was limited to very few German installations. Eventually, in January 1945 by an order from Hitler, top secret experimental information on radar, guided missiles, and jet propulsion was finally released.

However, many of these belated consignments, as with some earlier transfers, were lost while en route by blockage runner to Japan. In the case of the Me 163, complete specimens and details were released to the Japanese military attaché, but only undetailed data ever reached Japan.

CHANNELS OF SUPPLY

The main supply channels for interchange of information and material between Europe and the Far East were:
- Blockade Runners, both surface and submarines.
- Mail by courier and parcel post, presumably through diplomatic channels.
- Rail communication through Siberia. Quantity traffic by rail across Siberia was closed with the opening of the Russo-German war, but nevertheless, passage of personnel still continued after that date.

In addition, the use of long range aircraft was fully considered. One Italian aircraft in 1941 made a round trip to Tokyo. Thereafter, Germany negotiated for the opening of northern air route between Europe and the Far East. Japan, however, opposed this in favour of a southern route to avoid infringement of Soviet neutrality. Because of this difference of opinion, and the lack of long-range German transports, no such flights were carried out.

In the period 1941-1943 a large volume of two way shipments was carried out by surface blockade runners. . The cessation of surface running and the subsequent loss of the French Atlantic coast ports to submarine greatly restricted interchange of material and information during 1944-45. Although some submarines successfully made the trip during this latter period, the limited cargo space available restricted the material sent to Japan to blueprints. plans, small prototypes, and special material, carrying the highest priority. Unfortunately for the Japs, the severe restrictions in blockade running coincided with Germany's release of the most important weapons.

RECIPROCAL AID

The Germans expected little or no return of technical assistance; (exclusive of torpedo weapons, Japan's contribution was almost entirely raw materials). Information concerning the Ta bomb had been voluntarily transferred, but was never adopted by the Luftwaffe. However, in the middle of 1944, urgent but futile requests were made for available Japanese anti-bomber weapons. Major Kobayshi, JAAF liaison engineer in Germany since 1941, was unofficially approached by General Marquat about such Nipponese developments but the Japs "had no suggestions of any kind to offer" (Kobayashi, incidentally, had purchased the manufacturing rights for the electric primer, including drawings, chemical samples, and jigs. These items however, shipped by submarine, never reached Japan.

JAAF PURCHASES

Some of the material received by the Japanese Army Air Force included:
Specimen Aircraft:
* Focke-Wulf 190
* Messerschmitt 109
* Messerschmitt 210.

Aircraft Guns:
* 7.92mm (Mg-15) Produced as the Type 98.
* 13 mm machine gun (Mg 131)
* 15mm machine gun (Mauser Mg 151/15)
* 20mm machine gun (Mauser Mg 151/20)
  800 of these guns, purchased along with 400,000 rounds of German ammunition, were shipped by blockade runner in November 1943, subsequently installed in the Ki-61 (Tony), and employed in combat.

Bombsights:
* Lotfe 7C and 7D (Zeiss)

JNAF PURCHASES

The Japanese Naval Air Force also utilised the Daimler-Benz design in the construction of their Ha-60 Atsuta engines (model 21-Aeia 1185 hp, model 31 Aeip 1380 hp, model Aeit 1480 hp). The presence of three Daimler-Benz company technical representatives in Japan during the entire war accounts for the extensive use of this design. The following additional purchases were completed:
Specimen aircraft:
* Junkers 88. Used as a model in the original plans for the Ginka (Frances) medium bomber.

Aircraft guns:
* 7.92mm machine gun (Mg-15) Produced as the type 1.
* 7.92mm machine gun (Mg-I7)
* 13mm machine gun (Mg-131).
  The Japanese Navy's type 2 machine gun and ammunition were close copies of the German specimen, but the electric primer was not employed.
* 30mm machine cannon (Mk 108)

In the spring of 1944, the GAF presented to Japan as a gift, two Mk *108's* and, sample ammunition. Thereafter, both the Army and Navy became active in negotiations for further guns and ammunition of this and the Mk 103. Specimens were released in Germany: One Mk 108, cases of ammunition and drawings were captured on the U-234; other samples are believed to have been sunk en route to Japan.

The jet and rocket propulsion programme was based on meagre information received of German operational types:
- Shusui = version of Me 163.
- Kikka = version of Me 262
- Baika = version of Fzg 76 (VI)]

JOINT ARMY NAVY LIAISON
A joint army-navy technical committee was founded in Japan to coordinate all German technical material for both the army and the navy; but despite this set-up, duplication of inquiry continued. The Germans commented on this state of affairs, pointing out that they had no intention of making agreements separately with the two services, and that it would seem advisable for one service to take complete charge of negotiations.
As a result of later discussions, it was decided in the field of jet propulsion that the Navy would assume responsibility for negotiations with Germany. In spite of this understanding, however, the Army continued to maintain direct contact with the Germans,.

GERMAN RAW MATERIALS
Varying quantities of mercury, special steels, aluminium, lead, platinum, industrial diamonds, ball bearings and industrial chemicals were purchased by the Japs and shipped to the Far East.

Kyushu J7W Shinden
Navy Interceptor

Guided by the design of this Daimler-Benz engine, and by additional specimens of the DB 603, the Ha-40, Ha-140, and Ha-240 were test produced. The Kawasaki liquid-cooled engine Ha-40 (used in the Ki-61 Tony) is an improved copy of the obsolete German DB 601 for which manufacturing rights were purchased in 1939. , Prototypes of later type German engines never arrived in the Far East

Yokosuka R2Y Keiun
Navy Reconnaissance

4. AIRCRAFT

GENERAL CONCEPTS

The Japanese desire for light, manoeuvrable fighters resulted, initially, in short range types. Due to the brief distances involved in the pre-Pearl Harbour conflicts on the Asiatic Continent, the Japanese bombers, too, were planned with a short operational radius. Even after the initiation of the Greater East Asia War, range was not materially increased. As a result, the Japanese Army Air Force was incapable of attacking our long-range bases (B-29s on Marianas). Due to the exigencies of the sea operations, the range of most Navy aircraft was far superior; but the Japanese offensive complex seriously handicapped Navy reconnaissance when the tide turned, because of the unsuitability of these offensive aircraft to the reconnaissance role.

There was a dire need for a satisfactory long range bomber. The new Army heavy bomber, Type 4 (Peggy), was typically uneconomical. The original plans called for a bomb capacity of 3,000 kilograms (6615 pounds). The final model permitted only a 1000 kilogram (2205 pound) bomb load; less than half of the B-26 capacity. The air forces of the Japanese Army and Navy suffered a vicious limitation in air warfare, resulting from the lack of a satisfactory long range bomber on relatively equal terms to the opposing air forces.

Though operational Japanese bombers were generally limited to the direct supporting role of surface forces, it was soon realised that a large strategic bomber would be advantageous. A super bomber (Fugako) was designed which was capable of attacking the industrial centre of the United States, but the plan was dropped when the Ministry of Munitions calculated that, due to the raw material shortage, such production would interfere with the more essential new model fighters.
Nevertheless, just prior to the war's end, the Army and Navy combined efforts to produce a new long range bomber; which arrived too late.

ARMAMENT AND ARMOUR

In the early stages of the war, the prevailing dogfights made a highly manoeuvrable fighter quite advantageous. Early fighter types had no armour plate and the Japanese pilots often removed wing guns in order to increase manoeuvrability. However, when pilot quality deteriorated and losses were high in 1943, it was decided to apply armour and leak proofing to all new designs. At this same period came the trend towards heavier firepower.

Japanese bombers, likewise, started out under armed and remained so throughout the war. Their use of single .30 or .50 calibre flexible guns as a defence against American fighters mounting four to six heavier guns, paralleled the situation found earlier in the ETO where the Eighth AF heavies had to bear the brunt of attacks by heavily armed German fighters with far superior fire power.

The Japanese lack of bullet-proof tanks was a, serious handicap especially in view of the Allied emphasis on incendiary ammunition. The Japanese gave up the possibility of a successful leak proof tank as a futile quest. After unsuccessful combat tests of various types, most tanks were abandoned as too complicated and troublesome. The best leak proof types were too heavy and bulky for light airframes.

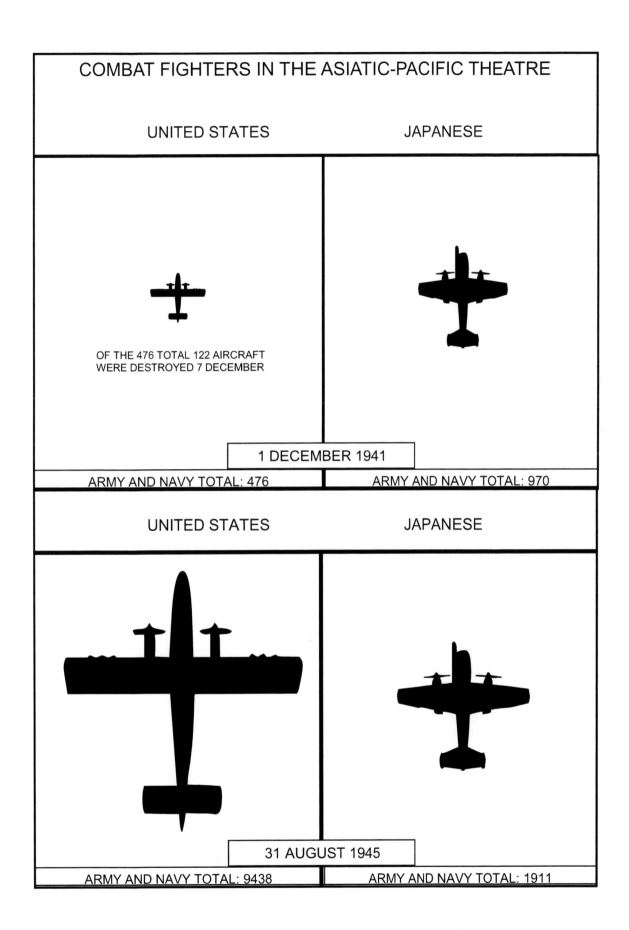

COMBAT FIGHTERS IN THE ASIATIC-PACIFIC THEATRE

UNITED STATES   JAPANESE

OF THE 476 TOTAL 122 AIRCRAFT
WERE DESTROYED 7 DECEMBER

1 DECEMBER 1941

ARMY AND NAVY TOTAL: 476   ARMY AND NAVY TOTAL: 970

UNITED STATES   JAPANESE

31 AUGUST 1945

ARMY AND NAVY TOTAL: 9438   ARMY AND NAVY TOTAL: 1911

Fig A

ENGINES

Japanese engines offered the most prominent performance handicap. Even when basically sound in design and satisfactory in original form, the mass produced engine was often the most serious deficiency of the Japanese aircraft, The quality. of factory workmanship had deteriorated to such an extent in the final months of the war that the naval air arsenal undertook to re-inspect minutely as many engines as possible before installation on aircraft.

The Nakajima 1,800 hp radial, air cooled engine is a compact, high-power unit and its designers, as well as the manufacturers were given technical honours. The amazing performance data caused both the Army and Navy to vie for this engine. The production at the Musashino factory was pushed. The Army fitted this engine to the newest fighter, Type 4 (Frank), but the production result, not only fell below the performance expectations, but it also introduced serious maintenance problems. The Navy, too, tried using these engines on their best planes and encountered similar problems.

Patent rights for Kawasaki's liquid cooled 1,350 hp, inverted V engine were originally bought from Germany and the engine manufactured at the Akashi plant. Difficulties in this production held up the operational use of the Type 3 fighter (Tony) and the inherent defects of the.. engine seriously handicapped the fighter's performance. Finally, Tony was. hurriedly equipped with the Mitsubishi 1,350 hp engine. This aircraft demonstrated excellent combat capabilities during a carrier attack on Kyushu. Minus the early engine difficulties, the Tony probably would have proven highly efficient in the Philippines and Okinawa campaigns.

Small model "0" high-horsepowered engines especially proved unreliable. Mitsubishi had a 2,200 hp, air cooled engine in this category which passed acceptance for use in the new type long range heavy bomber. Due to difficulties with this engine, the bomber was delayed an additional six months thereby precluding its use in attacks against the Marianas

Considerable progress was made by the Japanese. during the course of the war. Despite this advance, however, Jap engine performance continued to lag far behind the United States. This deficiency in turn inflicted severe limitations on armour and armament capacity:

Nakajima Sakae

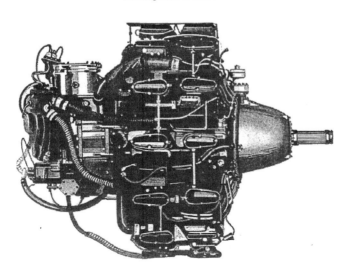

This engine powered several versions of the carrier- based Mitsubishi AGM Reisen fighter, the immortal Zero. The Sakae ('Pros-perity') was improved through several models, the output of the final series reaching the 1.100-1.200 hp range. This double-row 14-cylinder engine had a two-stage supercharger. Capacity was 27.8 litres. and the compression ratio was 7: 1. The diameter was 3 ft 8_in (114.4cm),length 5ft 2_in "(160 cm). and dry weight about 1,200lb (533kg).

HIGH ALTITUDE SUPERCHARGER DEVELOPMENT

Turbo-supercharger. Basic Japanese research was initiated by the Army about 20 years ago, when one turbo-supercharger purchased from France was subject to numerous ground and air tests. However, after a short period of experimentation all interest was abandoned.

More than 10 years elapsed before interest in the turbo supercharger was reinstated by a civilian agency; Mitsubishi Heavy Industries, in 1937. In 1940, military research was revised with studies of two foreign turbo superchargers, the American Moss and the Swiss Brown ball-bearing type. All Japanese supercharger development lagged, but Mitsubishi, far ahead of the Army and Navy, produced two prototype (1000 hp) turbo-superchargers. However, performance demand of aircraft had by then risen, so these early models were never installed and consequently further production was abandoned.

However, research was spurred on by the receipt of reports of successful American installations in the B-17 and P-43. By the end of 1942, Mitsubishi produced components for two 1500hp turbo-superchargers, designated the Ru-302. The first of these having passed the endurance test in the spring of 1943 were assembled and five each supplied to the Army and Navy. Eventually in April 1944, they were put into production and about 250 of them were manufactured by the end of the war.

The prototype of the 2000 hp model, Ru-303 was completed by the end of 1943. After one year, 15 were completed and distribution was made: 10 to the Army; and 5 to the Navy. Production began at the end of 1944 and by the close of the war 100 were produced.

Two-stage supercharger. Research on the two stage mechanical supercharger began in 1937. Both the Army and Mitsubishi studied the French Falcon supercharger. The design and construction of a test model was completed in 1939, but as numerous metallurgical problems arose, the research was temporarily halted. In 1941, in view of the relative advances in turbo supercharger development, the two-stage type was considered a secondary project. Later experimentation, using a Rolls-Royce engine as a test model, was undertaken but never reached perfection. Nevertheless, it was hoped to have a prototype installation on the Shiden Navy fighter by the end of 1943.

Ru-302 turbo-supercharger vs. single-stage two speed type. Raiden. With the Ru-302 at low altitudes the maximum speed fell about 20 knots (23 miles per hour). As the altitude increased, the difference decreased, but up to 7000 metres (22,967 feet), the speed was still below that of the single stage two speed supercharger installation. Under ideal conditions between 9000 metres (29,529 feet) and 11000 metres (36091 feet), an increase of 15 knots (17.28 mph) was registered. This unsatisfactory performance resulted in the abandonment of the installation.

Ki-46 type IV On this twin-engine fighter (originally designed for reconnaissance) at 9000 metres the turbo supercharger raised the speed from 314 to 341 knots (362 to 393 mph) The rate of climb up to 10,000 metres (32,810 feet) was about the same for the two types of superchargers.. Due to the frequent occurrence of problems with the engine proper, aggravated by lack of supercharger installation technique, the turbo supercharged engine never became operational. By the end *of* 1945, however, it was expected that installation would begin on the following .
aircraft types;

Ki-46 type IV (Ru-302) * Ki-83 (Ru 303) * Ki-74 (Ru 303) * Reppu (improved type) (Ru 303)

It was also desired and planned to install turbo superchargers on the following additional aircraft;

Ki-87 * Ki-94 * Ki-00 (model 2) * Ki-102A

Conclusion

(1) The use of high altitude superchargers on operational aircraft could have raised the critical altitude rating from the present average of 6000 metres (19,686 feet) to an average of 8000 metres (26,250 feet) with two-stage superchargers, and to an average of 10000 metres (32,1310 feet) with turbo superchargers; the maximum critical altitude predicted by the Japanese was 11,400 metres (37,400 feet). With the limited boost pressure used in Japanese engines, these high figures were quite possible.

(2) The failure in early developments of a suitable high-altitude supercharger, along with the generally poor performance of the engine, not only handicapped existing tactics, but, furthermore, precluded the operational use of many potentially effective and highly developed anti-bomber measures, including air to air bombing, parachute and cable bombing

FIGHTER CONCEPT AND DEVELOPMENT

In January 1938, at a combined military and civilian research meeting sponsored by Mitsubishi, it was decided that manoeuvrability should be given first consideration in fighter plane design. Thus was initiated the emphasis on the advantageous dog-fight tactics with little provision for self-defence. The early Jap successes seemed to confirm this theory. With but scant recognition of Jap numerical superiority and the excellent battle-trained pilots, almost all of the credit was given to the Zeke, which was more manoeuvrable and could climb higher and faster than opposition types. All forward planning of fighter aircraft was fatally delayed by this early and sustained belief by the General Staff in the invincibility of the Zeke, especially in view of its low rate of operational losses.
Up until near the end of the war, despite increasing Allied success in attack and retrieve methods, this now obsolete tactical concept was adhered to religiously. Maintenance of superior manoeuvrability imposed grave handicaps upon armour and armament. As the war progressed the need for greater fire power and defensive armour became more and more evident.

Steps were finally taken to increase the armament; but the inherent increase in gross weight and drag cut down on the performance so materially that engine power had to be increased. Despite numerous power plant modifications which increased field maintenance by many hours, in addition to increasing production time and delaying new types; it was usually found necessary to design a new improved engine.

Often, Army and Navy requirements on speed, range and manoeuvrability so exceeded the factory capabilities that much time was lost. (In the case of the Ki-83 two years elapsed due to this lack of a concrete plan). The first instructions were issued in May 1941, but it was not until May 1943 that the final plan was reached and an experimental order issued). Much was learned from the numerous combat trials of the many modified types and these lessons were later embroiled in new and efficient designs. However, the great majority of these more satisfactory production models were not decided upon until just before the closing of the war.

The Naval arsenal design staff had early envisaged the need for a successor to the Zeke, and had in mind a fighter like the Sam. When the General Staff finally saw the need for a replacement, it was found that engine design was lagging behind that of air frames so that delay in building a properly engined test model of Sam resulted. George 11 was finally pushed into combat as a stop gap. Later, despite delays in developing George 21, the parallel work on Sam lagged even further behind, thereby forcing the mass production of the former. This production stage, however, was reached too late to be of practical assistance in stemming the rising Allied air power. Likewise, turbo supercharger problems on Jack and engine problems on the Zeke 04 made these two aircraft ineffective. Development of twin-engined interceptors was equally discouraging because of insufficient speeds attained, and soon fuel and engine production made the twin-engined fighter uneconomical for further trial. The Denko was expected to fill the long felt need for a pure night fighter but was fatally delayed due to a poor initial airframe design by the less efficient Aichi organisation.

Though basic aircraft design was not always inadequate, the mass product was often of poor quality. This fact, coupled with the ever increasing Japanese use of substitute materials and low octane fuel, made it almost impossible to improve performance of existing types.

Nevertheless, the continued belief in the invincibility of the light manoeuvrable fighter resulted in unreasonable demands for the modification of these operational types in efforts to cope with new Allied aircraft. The. outcome was that the rapidly multiplying modification problems gave priority on technical research to the old models and fatally delayed the development of urgently needed new types.

HEAVY BOMBERS
The first operational four engine bomber, the Shinzan (Liz), was abandoned in December 1941 due to its failure to meet the planned requirements. The radius of action was shorter than anticipated and the top speed was inadequate. The production results of the most recent heavy bomber, the Rita, indicated that the building of heavy bombers might be beyond the scope of the Japanese aircraft industry, since little volume could be expected from inadequate production facilities.

Nevertheless, the construction of super bombers was contemplated in 1943 by both the Army and the Navy, with the view of bombing the United States. This six -engined bomber, the Fugaku, designed by Nakajima, was to be capable of carrying 4 metric tons (8,800 pounds) of bombs over a 10,000 mile range of 13000 metres altitude (42,650 feet). It was to be slightly larger than the B-29, with a wing span of 60 metres (197 feet). The planned speed at altitude was to be 650-680 kilometres (404-423 miles per hour).

The Army's plan was for the Fugaku to do strategic bombing in the United States and then go on to Germany. There was to be a crew of only five and the armament was to be negligible. Only two guns, calibre .50 were to be installed, one each in nose and tail turrets with Sperry computing gun sights. It was considered that the contemplated 45,000 to 50,000 feet of altitude would keep the bomber practically free from interception.

The Navy plan was to take off from Misawa field in northern Honshu, bomb the United States Pacific coast, and return home. The Navy's Fugaku would carry a crew of seven, and the total defences would be four 20mm guns.

The development of the Fugaku reached only the model testing stage. With the front line continually closing in on the home island, the Japanese decided to follow the example of the Spitfire's defence of London, and emphasis was shifted to fighter aircraft.

PHOTO RECONNAISSANCE PROBLEMS
The lack of a suitable fast high-altitude photo recce was first felt by the Navy in the battles of the Solomons. Army Dinahs at Rabaul were accordingly taken over to provide the needed data. In the final phase of the war in Kyushu, four or five Ki-46's with army crews were placed under command of the 171st air group at Kanoya for reconnaissance duty. The Navy air command, upholding the general Navy view that army aircrew navigation training was inferior, claimed that the inaccurate fixes on the sightings of Allied task forces was causing great confusion.

Proportion of development program devoted toward the improvement of existing models, to the neglect of development of new fighters

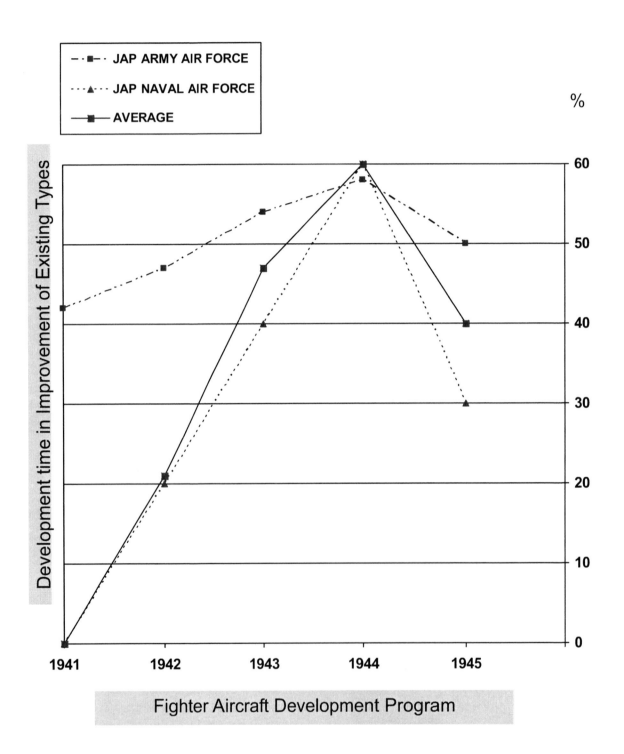

Fig B

The turn of the war from offence to defence introduced new problems which necessitated the commitment of Myrt to operational use even before it had been flight tested. Plans then centred upon Riyi, in which the fundamentals of Frances were preserved to hasten production. However, with the retreat towards the homeland, the need of a very long range reconnaissance waned and the, project was soon abandoned. It was hoped that successful installation of a turbo-supercharger in the Myrt would fill the new requirements, but tests were not completed until the final days of the war.

THE ALUMINIUM SHORTAGE

Wooden Aircraft. As a means of meeting the aluminium shortage, it was expected that the inherent craftsmanship of the Japanese wood-working industry could be harnessed to wooden aircraft manufacture. Starting with a wooden training model of Val, the Navy expected to build an operational suicide version, to be followed by a wooden Betty (Taiyo), Tabby (DC3) and Soku, a large 40 ton flying boat. The lack of both current supplies and future manufacturing potential of special wood working machinery for aircraft construction, however, portended a lengthier and more expensive production programme than had been foreseen. The Army succeeded in building an all-wooden fighter, ki-106; it's weight proved excessive, however, and steps were being taken to reduce this weight at the end of the war. Research was also carried out on the construction of wood tail surfaces for other aircraft; and wooden rudders, stabilisers etc, were tested on operational types. (German assistance was received in the form of special material and adhesives for wood aircraft)

Steel Aircraft. The Navy had steel versions of Frances and Rita on the project board, the metal research being done by Kawanishi. The Army's project for a steel aircraft, Ki-113, was dropped when production facilities appeared lacking. However, practical data was being worked up to utilise steel in the design of parts for other aircraft.

Aluminium from clay A Japanese scientist Professor limori, developed a method of extracting aluminium from low-grade ore. From dry loam he was able to attain 7 to 8 per cent aluminium. The Japanese Board of Technology examined the procedure, but decided it was too expensive, and the project was suspended.

ALCOHOL AS FUEL

With the reduced petroleum supplies, the Japanese began in October 1944 to adapt their aircraft for the use of grain alcohol (made from potatoes and sugar) to replace gasoline. Alcohol, because of its high-oxygen content, has a heating value much lower than that for gasoline. Nevertheless, because of its ability to withstand a very high compression and to recover a greater quantity of waste heat during vaporisation, it can deliver almost as much power per pound of fuel as can gasoline. Although it has not yet been economically possible to use alcohol in the United States, it has been widely used in Europe and in tropical countries.

Operational use. The alcohol plants were turning out only enough fuel to supply the trainers when the war ended, and most of the training aircraft were so converted. It was the intention of the Japanese to convert all types of planes to alcohol except special-purpose a/c Shortcomings. Despite regulations to the contrary, it was often noted that alcohol fuel supplies were frequently used for drinking purposes by military personnel. In addition, the following aircraft deficiencies resulted from this substitute fuel:

- Lower performance
- Greater installed weight
- Reduced Range
- Extra maintenance problems

Nakajima Kikka Navy Attack Bomber

5. JET PROPULSION & ROCKET

Mitsubishi J8M1 Shusui Army Interceptor

GENERAL

Japanese research on jet propulsion was begun by the Army and Navy, independently, in 1941 and 1942, respectively. It was not until 1943, after receipt of intelligence reports on foreign developments, that these projects were accelerated.

JOINT ARMY-NAVY EFFORTS.

In 1944, inter-service cooperation was seen as a dire necessity in order to utilize fully the few available jet technicians, conserve critical materials, and minimise on the number of plane models.

The Ki-102, Kikka (Me 262 type) was almost wholly a Navy project utilising the Ne-20 (Oka 43 type) engine. The Army rendered some little assistance in the preparation of the test model.

In the development of the Ki-200 Shusui (Me 163 type) there is found an all-out effort for full cooperation. Joint research was conducted, and the Army and Navy set up a civilian research committee. The Navy was designated as primarily responsible for the assembly, and the Army was to develop the engine (chemical rocket). During the course of this programme, Japanese anti aircraft force engineers presented some army views on the airframe design, but these ideas were given no consideration in the Navy development plans. The Army, as a result, undertook the design of an improved Shusui called Ki-202. Meanwhile, the Navy initiated a power plant development project of its own, and as a result the Army and Navy each came out with separate engines. Though an abortive attempt at coordination, nevertheless, in this project the Army and Navy probably reached their peak of cooperation.

TACTICAL CONCEPTS

The primary application of jet and rocket propulsion was .towards the development of special attack aircraft. In addition to the operational and pending Navy Oka developments, the next important jet project was the production of the Ki-201 (Jap version of the German Me 262). This was considered, in the light of German intelligence reports, to be the most superior of the proposed non-conventional types. In addition to it's Kamikaze value against surface vessels, it was planned to profit from the Nazi successes by using it as an antifighter pursuit aircraft. To supplement the special attack role of the Kikka, another Kamikaze jet type similar to the German piloted V1 was pending development: This was the Baika, still in the design stage. (Not to be confused with the operational Oka "Baka")

The secondary tactical application was the rocket propelled B-29 interceptor. This was to be the sole function of the Ki-200 and Ki-202 (Navy and Army versions of the German Me-163)

A subordinate application of the jet engine was proposed by the Navy. This was a plan to utilise the best available turbine-jet engine in the reconnaissance plane Keiun.

PLANNED OPERATIONAL EMPLOYMENT

As the Army had the task of protecting the mainland, they were to receive the larger percentage of the aircraft produced.

The Army originally planned to use the Shusui (Ki-200) as an interceptor in certain key areas. Experiments were expected to be completed by March 1945, with production between April 1945 and March 1946 totalling 2,400 planes. These Shusui would then be used to activate 10 Hikosenti (36 planes per Sentai) and were to be based first in the Tokyo area; then in the Nagoya-Osaka area, the northern part of Kyushu, and one element in Manchuria. As previously noted, they were to be used solely against B-29s.

Two or three Hikosenti of Kikka (Ki-20 1)were expected to be activated by March 1946 for use against enemy aircraft and shipping.

KIKKA DEVELOPMENT
By the early part of 1944, a turbine jet with centrifugal compressor had been completed, later modified by the addition of a four stage axial flow blower, and designated the Ne-12B. Two Ne-12Bs were intended to be used in the anti-invasion fighter-bomber Kikka but the airframe was ahead of the engine development. In May 1944, photographic prints of the German BMW 003 co-axial turbojet arrived by submarine (Complete plans were in another which was sunk). Though 40 of the Ne-12Bs were produced, the production was given up in favour of developing a Ne-20 based on the German designed BMW 003:

In early August 1945 Kikka made a successful test flight using the newly adapted Ne-20. The test results were;
    Sea level.
*   End. 37 mins at 375 mph.
    20,000ft
*   End. 49 mins at 420 mph

SHUSUI DEVELOPMENT
At a conference held by the Japanese Navy in August 1944 the Mitsubishi representative was handed a copy of the German Me-163 manual and ordered to build an experimental Shusui, tailless single-seat interceptor. The design policy was to copy the Me-163 exactly except as follows: The Mk-103 30 mm cannons were to be replaced by the two new Navy type 17 30mm; and Japanese Navy instruments and other accessories were to be used.

The first test flight, on 7 July 1945, resulted in a crash landing due to a failure of the fuel feed system. The fuel system was soon corrected, two more were assembled, and several others nearly completed when the war ended. Characteristics for the Shusui were as follows:

*   Take off time   11 seconds
*   Take off run   1050 feet
*   Level flight range 4 minutes.

 The Shusui Ki-200 and Ki-202) was powered by the Toku-ro

No 2 bichemical rocket which depended upon the reaction of fluid "A" (80 percent oxygen) on fluid "B" (mixture of methanol, hydrogen, and water)

BAKAI
Research into pulsating-type jets had only just started at the Navy air technical arsenal. Initial tests with benzol as fuel had been made to determine thrust developed, using an auxiliary blower to produce the required flow of air. Provisional plans called for the jet to be used in Baika, the airframe which was to be developed by Kawanishi, and probably closely patterned after the German piloted V1. Its primary tactical purpose was to effect Kamikaze attacks against vessels nearing the Japanese mainland.

Outstanding features of this plane were to be:

a. Small dimensions and light weight. Wing area 7.59 M2. Weight 1430kg (3153 lbs)
b. Engine to utilise crude pine-root oil, to offset expected loss of refineries.
c. Simple construction, to offset expected lower skill of workmen.
d. Built of relatively easily obtainable wood and steel, to offset lower production of dural and aluminium alloys_ 33

KEIUN

At the time the Ne-20 jet engine project was initiated by the Navy the BMW 003 principles were given to Tsikajima-Shibaura Company Hidachi-Nakajima, and Mitsubishi, and each proceeded independently in the development of the Ne-130, Ne-230, and Ne-330 respectively. These three turbojets were in approximately the same state of completion at the war's end, but none had actually flown. The best of the three was intended to be used in the reconnaissance plane Keuin. This aircraft was originally designed to take the Ha-70 model 01 engine, two conventional Atsutas coupled together, and had actually flown with this unusual installation.

CONCLUSIONS

In general, the Japanese may be said to have made fair progress in the field of jet and rocket propulsion despite the following handicaps:

- Development programmes were initiated at a very late date
- Most specimens and detailed data were lost while en route to Japan by submarine, and little detailed technical assistance was furnished by the Germans.
- Major metallurgical problems were encountered in the production of metals capable of withstanding the terrific speed and heat of the jet engines.
- The administration remained firm in its decision not to interrupt production of conventional engines for conversion to jets.

Yokosuka MXY7 Oka (Baika) Navy Suicide Aircraft

JET AND ROCKET ENGINES

Name	Type	Revolutions per minute	Length	Diameter	Weight	Thrust	Fuel Comsumption
			Millimeters	*Millimeters*	*Kilograms*	*Kilograms*	*Light/hours*
Ne-20 (Kikka) (Oka 43)	Turbo-jet	11,000	2,700 mm	620 mm	470 kg	475 kg	900
Ne-130	Turbo-jet	9,000	3,850	850	900	900	1,600
Ne-230	Turbo-jet	8,100	3,430	914 and 762	870	885	1.630
Ne-330	Turbo-jet	7,600	4,000	1,180 and 880	1,200	1,300	2,530
Toku-Ro 2 (Shusui)	Biochemical Rocket	Pump rev 14,500	2,500	900 x 650	170	1,500 (4 min)	T-6.7 C-2.0 (kg/sec)
TSU-11 (Oka 22)	Engine-jet	Engine 3,000, fan 9,000	2,200	640	200	200	1,200
KA (Baika)	Pulsating jet	—	3,700	580	150	300	1,600
Style 4, No 1, model 20 (Oka 11)	Solid Fuel Rocket	—	1,200	255	115 (Oka x 3)	800 (9 sec) (Oka x 3)	44 kg (9 sec)

Fig C

BAIKA
FZG-76 (V-1)

German Piloted

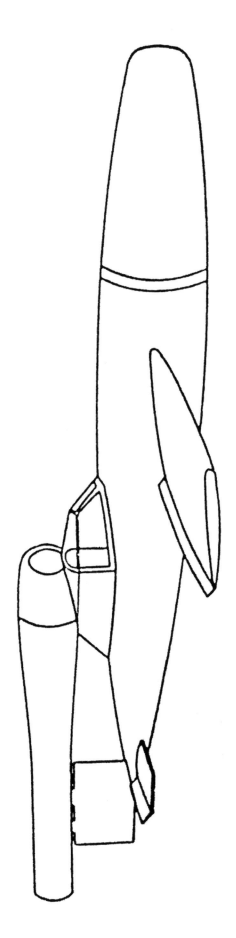

5. SPECIAL ATTACK

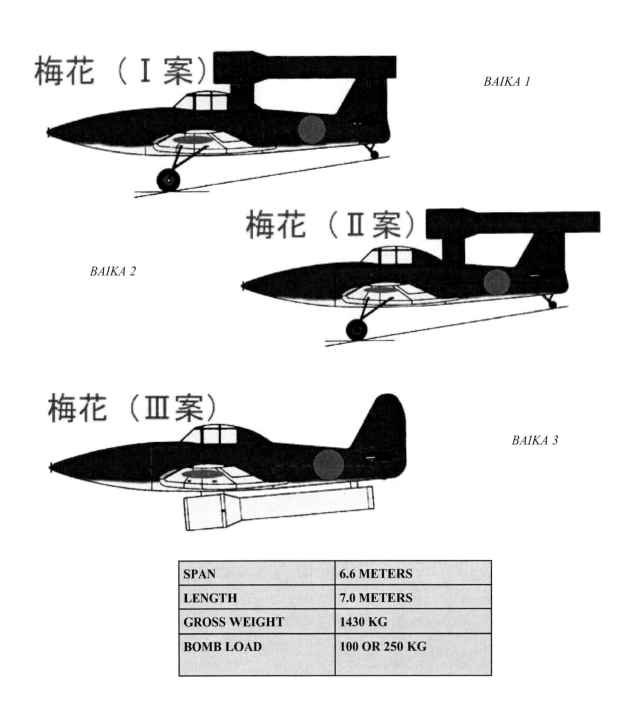

梅花（Ⅰ案）

BAIKA 1

梅花（Ⅱ案）

BAIKA 2

梅花（Ⅲ案）

BAIKA 3

SPAN	6.6 METERS
LENGTH	7.0 METERS
GROSS WEIGHT	1430 KG
BOMB LOAD	100 OR 250 KG

DESIGNS UNDER CONSIDERATION FOR THE BAIKA

Fig D

THE SUICIDE TRADITION IN JAPAN,
"The quick falling cherry blossom, that lives but a day and dies with destiny fulfilled,
Is the brave spirit of Samurai youth
Always ready, his fresh young strength
To offer to his lord"
Ancient Japanese poem,

From the traditional Japanese cherry blossom was chosen the symbol of Samurai spirit - "willingness to die young and vigorous, rather than to live and fade" The uniforms of the Army and Navy for years have carried conventional cherry blossoms on the badges; and based on this same tradition the name Sakura (cherry blossom) was adopted as the official Japanese nomenclature for the suicide bomb.

ARMY KAMIKAZE CONCEPT
Despite the time-worn tradition. General Masaki, who supervised the design of the army suicide bomb, characterised the Sakura as a final desperate, but efficient, measure. "When the degree of mastery of the air is equally divided between the opposing forces, planes should be used for the purpose for which they were originally intended. However, when the strength of the enemy forces becomes overwhelming I believe it is scientifically more efficient to adopt Kamikaze tactics." Towards the end of the war few bombers returned from orthodox attacks, this being the same reason for the Japanese Anti aircraft Force conversion to Kamikaze.

NAVY KAMIKAZE CONCEPT
The Navy's Sakura (Oka), nicknamed Baka (fool) by the Allies, was planned following the widespread story of a highly patriotic lieutenant junior grade, Ota, who was said to have sunk an Allied aircraft carrier with a "single strike", crashing his body with his plane". After the Japanese defeat in Saipan, the theory prevailed among th younger naval officers that there was no way to intercept the "tidal attack of the United States fleets" except by executing the "death-defyng, body-crashing attack" From this idea evolved the so-called Kamikaze special attack forces.

NAVY SAKURA (OKA) DEVELOPMENT
The Navy Oka recorded the most rapid development in Japanese annals. The designers in the first naval air technical arsenal impressed deeply by Ota's patriotism, worked day and night and completed the design in one month. Splendid cooperation was likewise shown between the Navy arsenal and subcontractors, and ten experimental models were rapidly built.

The original Oka was to be released from the under part of the fuselage of a land-based torpedo bomber at a point not liable to interception by the enemy deck fighters. If pursued by fighters after release, it could evade them by high speed diving plus rocket acceleration. It was in reality a high speed piloted glide bomb. Some additional features stressed by the authorities were:
a.   Ability to sink an aircraft carrier with a "single blow".
B.   Very simplified construction, coupled with use of easily obtainable materials.
       Oka 11 (Propulsion: three solid fuel rocket units)

The initial model was named Oka 11, and production began in September 1944. Strict secrecy was maintained, although the workmen were told the purpose of the plane in order to raise.enthusiasm. Within 2 or 3 months it was planned to ship these weapons to the Phillipine theatre aboard the aircraft carrier "Shinano", but the plan fell through when the carrier was- sunk by submarine torpedo attack off Tosa. ,

In the operations off Formosa the Baka appeared for the first time. All the mother planes were shot down by defending US Navy Hellcats,' and were unable to get within reach of the US task forces. This operation revealed the two principal defects: the insufficient range of the missile; and the below-par performance of its mother aircraft, the Betty.

1. Oka 22 (Propulsion: Internal combustion engine-jet)

With an eye toward eliminating these defects, a modified type, the Oka 22 was designed. This plane was smaller and lighter than its prototype, and fitted with a Tsu 11 engine jet. The long range Ginga (Frances11) with flying characteristics superior to the Betty, was designated the mother plane. The range of the model 22 was 40 nautical miles (46 miles) at sea level, and 70 nautical miles (80.6 miles) when released from 4000 metres (13,124 feet) altitude. Fifty planes were manufactured by the designers at the first naval air technical arsenal, but these aircraft never reached the operational stage due to non-completion of test flights.

2. Oka 30, 40 and 50 series (Propulsion: coaxial turbojet)

In the interim, the development of the 30, 40, and 50 series was in progress. These were all to employ a superior means of propulsion, namely the Ne-20 coaxial turbojet, the series differences being in the method of launching.

The 50 series was intended to be launched from the parent plane Rita whose development set-backs hindered the progress, Neither Betty nor Frances was deemed able to carry the greater weight of this series. Renzan (Rita), over twice the size of Betty, was designed specifically as the carrier for this Oka 30.

The 50 series had been projected for launching from a towplane. Runways, however, were generally too short to get the Oka airborne, and this series made little progress.

3. The 40 series.

The Oka 43 was designed by the Aichi Company to play the principal role. in the forthcoming decisive battle in the Japanese home islands. This model was intended to be launched from a land-_ased catapult 100 metres (328 feet in length). Due to its folding wings it could easily be stored underground. Had the war continued, this weapon, with its range of 100-115 nautical miles (127 -132 miles) might have presented quite a problem for the Allies.

4. Oka with floats.

Owing to the non-utilisation of numerous Oka 11 's, in the Singapore area, due to lack of parent aircraft, preliminary experiments were initiated, in equipping the Baka with seaplane floats. However the war ended before completion of the tests. These were intended to be posted under cover on the north and south shores at the eastern mouth of Johore Strait, and were to be employed for night attacks against enemy ships forcing their way into the strait.

The short range of the Oka 11 put close limitations upon its tactical value in this capacity. However, the later, longer-range Okas would have been well adapted for such operational modification and employment

Navy Sakura (Oka 11)

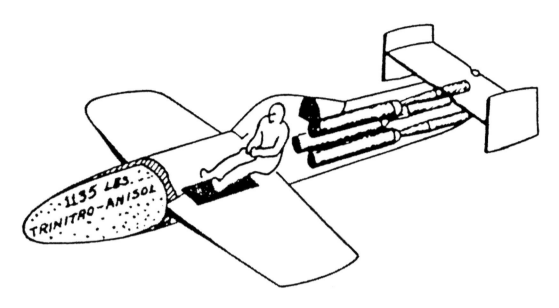

1135 LBS. TRINITRO-ANISOL

Fig E

	OKA 11	OKA 22	OKA 43
Manufacturer	1st Nata	1st Nata	AICHI
Type	3 Solid Fuel Rockets	TSU-11 Engine Jet	(Turbo-Jet NE 22)
Crew	1	1	1
Span	5.0	4.12	9.0
Length m	6.066	6.88	8.16
Heigh m	1.16	1.15	1.15
Wing Area	6.00m^2	4.00m^2	13.00m^2
Weight Empty	440 kg	545 kg	1150 kg
Normal Weight	2140 kg	1450 kg	2270 kg
Static Thrust	800 kg x 9 x 3	200 kg	475 kg
Fuel Capacity Ltr	——	290	400
Maximum Speed S.L.	——	230kt/hr	250 kt/hr
Range S. Mi	20@250 (4km)	70@240 (4km)	150@250 (4km)
Bomb kg	1200 x 1	600 x 1	800 x 1
Wing Load	351	363	175

5.Training Types

Modifications of the Oka 11 and 43, both solo and dual versions, were prepared for training purposes by the addition of skids and flaps. The Oka 11 was used, over Yokosuka Airfield, for gliding practice after release from a mother plane. The Oka 43 trainer was to have a powder-rocket (mean thrust 400kg (882lbs) burning time 9 seconds) installed in the rear of the fuselage in place of the turbine rocket. This latter type was to be catapulted from a rocket-propelled carriage; the launching to be made from a mountain top 600 metres (1968 feet) above and 3000 metres (9843 feet) away from the airfield destination.

ARMY SAKURA DEVELOPMENT

The development of an effective suicide bomb was more seriously retarded in the Army, on account of the exaggerated claims as to the results of Kamikaze attacks with orthodox aircraft and ordinary demolition bombs. Repeated reports were received claiming that such attacks had sunk large battleships. It was believed that these false reports were circulated to preserve civilian morale and to uphold the Samurai spirit as well as the Army's reputation.

The Army technicians were convinced that the ordinary Kamikaze could not sink a heavily armoured warship without a number of direct hits, and for this reason designed and perfected their powerful Sakura bomb for initial installation in the Ki-67 bomber. However, the continued receipt of false reports made this special weapon appear unnecessary, despite scientific opinion to the contrary. As a result only a few Ki-67's were prepared and none used operationally.

The akura type 1 was a 2,900 kg (6394.5lb) bomb with a ' hemispherical-shaped hollow charge. Extensive tests resulted in a very effective design possessing exceptional armour-piercing capabilities. The results of tests by the Army at Mito indicate that the Sakura, when detonated statically, had the following characteristics;

- Penetrated simultaneously four steel plates of 6, 40, 172 and 35 mm thickness, when detonated at an angle of 45 degrees.
- Penetrated simultaneously two steel plates of 240 and 400mm thickness, when detonated at an angle of 45 degrees. The resultant hole was 400 to 500 mm in diameter.
- Penetrated simultaneously four steel-reinforced concrete walls, alternately 1 metres (3.28ft) thick and one half metre (l064 feet) thick. The distance between the first and last walls was 18 metres *(59ft)*.

A modified model, the Sakura type 2, was designed to make a more compact warhead in order to fit the limitations on size because of the aircraft. Its effectiveness was somewhat less than the Sakura 1. Although it could penetrate the reinforced concrete walls when detonated at 90 degrees to the wall, it could not penetrate the fourth wall when detonated at an angle of 45 degrees. The weight of the 'Sakura 2 was 1300kg (2866lbs)

CONVENTIONAL AIRCRAFT MODIFIED FOR KAMIKAZE OPERATIONS
Aside from early impulsive suicide attacks, it was initially planned to utilise training types and obsolete operational models for Kamikaze. Ordinarily, the fighters would carry a single 250kg (550lb) demolition bomb, whereas aircraft of the Ki-51 class often carried a total of 800kg (l764lbs). Omitting the arming wire extension leading to the pilot's compartment, these conventional aircraft were generally unmodified.

Probably the only major "non return" mission modification was found on the Judy 43. This single seat version, employed in attacks against task forces, was fitted with accelerating rockets whose boost increased the speed by approximately 35 knots (40mph)

The Seiran submarine-borne float plane with a bomb load of one 800kg (1764lbs) bomb and capable of good performance, was a potent Kamikaze weapon which was used in 1-400 and 1-401 and being installed in 1-402, (three per submarine) and 1-14 (two per submarine). A special 30 metre (98ft) catapult was built into the submarines. Removal of the floats was planned to improve performance in future "no return" missions. The Nanzan, a land-based version, was constructed to simulate the launching condition in initial pilot training for catapulting.

PENDING KAMIKAZE DEVELOPMENTS
Development trends were in two principal directions. Utilisation *of* available materials. In this category were all-wooden aircraft, such as the Val. Efforts to utilise stocks of obsolete engines resulted in the roughly constructed Toka, a naval copy of the Army Ki-ll5.

Application of jet and rocket propulsion
In these development projects we find a belated and unfruitful attempt at "full" cooperation between the Army and Navy.

Kikka (Nakajima design) Twin engines jet aircraft planned for use as an anti invasion suicide bomber. The bomb capacity was 500 kg (1102lbs). This design was based on the German Me 262.

Baika (Navy and Kawanishi design) Research was being made into the pulsating-flow propulsive duct. Had this athodyd jet been developed successfully, it probably would have been used in considerable numbers as a piloted suicide weapon, having the great advantage *of* simplicity of production. (This was modelled after the German VI)

TACTICAL EFFECTIVENESS

In contemplation of the forthcoming invasion of the home islands, Lieutenant General Tazoe estimated, based on the Leyte and Okinawa experiences, that one out of four planes would sink or damage an Allied ship. This assessment gave due consideration to anticipated employment of all classes of aircraft coupled with the use of ordinary demolition bombs.

EVALUATION OF SUICIDE TACTICS

It is evident that a skilfully designed and tactfully employed suicide weapon may, in the long run, result in greater efficiency, due to the many advantages, some of which follow;

Greater potential damage to the target per aircraft attacking due to applicability of very large bomb loads, or by the optional employment of special bombs of the Army Sakura variety.
Alternate possibility of super long range on "no return" missions.
Comparatively little training required for direct hits, due to the proximity of the attacker and the relatively large target.
Greatly increased aircraft production, due to the generally simpler design. and elimination of fire control and other equipment, coupled with the applicability of short life substitute materials.

Army Sakura

The Army Sakrua Type—2 Incorporated in the K1-67 Bomber (Peggy)

Sakura 2

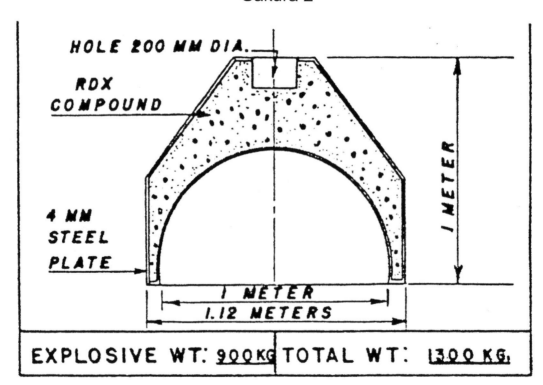

HOLE 200 MM DIA.

RDX COMPOUND

4 MM STEEL PLATE

1 METER

1 METER

1.12 METERS

EXPLOSIVE WT: 900 KG   TOTAL WT: 1300 KG.

Fig G

Effect of Sakura 1 upon Steel Plate

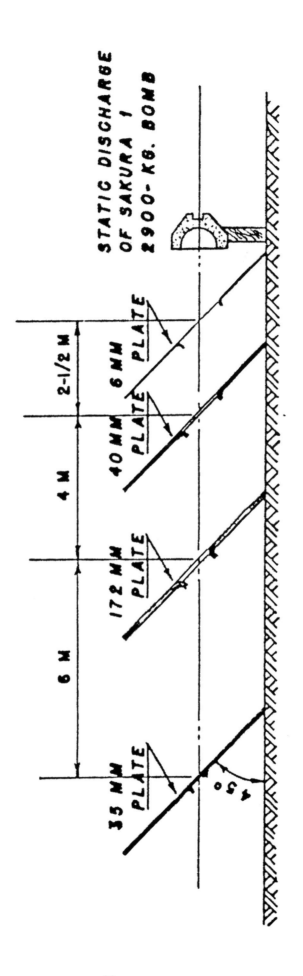

STATIC DISCHARGE OF SAKURA 1 2900-KG. BOMB

6 MM PLATE

40 MM PLATE

172 MM PLATE

35 MM PLATE

2-1/2 M

4 M

6 M

45°

Fig H

29.

Wider field of tactical employment due to the elimination of the need of return landing fields, plus the possibility of surprise launchings from parent ships or aircraft, or from unpredictable land or water locations.

DEFICIENCIES IN JAPANESE PLANNING

Despite the Sakura tradition, late planning in suicide tactics on the part of the Japanese initiated a great loss of efficiency due to the following weaknesses:

- Use of highly vulnerable aircraft of poor performance, resulting in. correspondingly low percentage of strikes.
- Lack of careful consideration of weapons vs target vulnerability (Use of relatively inefficient demolition bombs)
- Operational use of unperfected new weapons too early in the development stage, as with the Oka 11 (range too short, and parent aircraft too vulnerable).
- Use of makeshift special weapons, hastily designed and assembled, as with Toka, in attempt to absorb stocks of old materials.

Nakajima Ki-115 Tsurugi Army Suicide Aircraft

In the final stage of the war, all available aircraft had been prepared for "special attack" An Army unit at Itami alerted to attack an expected Allied flotilla on 17 August 1945, loaded Ki-61 fighters even to the extent of placing bombs in the cockpit with the pilots.

Nakajima Ki-84 Hayate (Frank) Army Interceptor

Nakajima K1-44 Shoki (Tojo) Army Fighter

Nakajima K1-43 Hayabusa (Oscar) Army Fighter

Aichi M6A Seiran Navy Attack Aircraft

The Hanger of the Japanese Aircraft carrying submarine of the aircraft above

7.   B-29 RAMMING ATTACKS

I-400 Japanese submarine carried three Seiran aircraft

GENERAL

In April 1945, after about 6 months of operational experiments, the Army Air Force adopted specific rules for suicide ramming attacks by orthodox fighters against B-29s. These tactics were based on sound scientific research as well as by a study of actual "Combat examples of body attacks".

TACTICAL PROCEDURE
Japanese pilots were primarily cautioned as to the tactical surprise advantage of making only one approach. They were given a thorough knowledge of the B-29, including flying characteristics, effective angles of attack, and vulnerable points of impact. To facilitate rapid ascent and greater manoeuvrability, machine guns and other dispensable equipment were removed. A special and detailed ground check was made on oxygen and communications equipment which were considered of vital importance to this type of mission.

Waiting Period
The fighters formed a "protective circumference" around the centre of the strategic area in which the attack was expected, and assigned positions to avoid confusion. Radio communications was maintained with the ground as well as with the other planes in the patrol sector.

Search and Contact
The entire 'Patrol was to execute a careful search and as soon as the enemy was detected the bombers' axis of flight was determined and the B-29s were approached along that line. Position was to be taken up swiftly; not overlooking the possibility. of launching the attack from the clouds, or utilising the position of the sun. Superior altitude was to be immediately gained and maintained.

Attack by single fighter.
The nose attack was' preferred not only because, of the amplification of the surprise element, but in view of the lesser firepower from that sector. It was deemed advisable to approach either from a position slightly above and ahead of the bomber close to the line of flight or directly head on. An approach from ahead and below was also considered satisfactory, but in all cases a high degree of mobility was demanded in the event that there was a major degree of deviation by the bomber near the end of the Tail attacks were to be avoided in view of the long exposure to the heavy fire power. The only exceptions to this rule were allowed when a bomber's guns jammed or when it ran out of ammunition, and where judgement was used in drawing the fire of the turrets.

The Collision
In a frontal approach, it was believed best to make the attack against the air flight compartments; in a rear or side approach' the empennage was to be selected as the target. During this nose attack it was considered advisable to throttle back in order to gain time. However, upon colliding the action was to take place in one swift movement, and it was determined desirable to incline the wing towards the vertical in order to increase the probability of a hit. Fighters were repeatedly warned against preliminary approaches which might induce "appropriate and radical evasive action" on the part of the bomber. A recommended angle of attack is shown in Figure K.

Mass attacks
Mass collisions promised the best results, so every effort was made to promote attacks in force. Fighters were instructed to maintain formation during the waiting period. Upon confirmation of the target by the Squadron Commander, instructions were given to the

Combat Examples of Ramming Attacks by Japanese Army Fighters against USAAF B-29 Bombers

Pilot's Name	Unit	A/C Type	Direction of Attack	Region of Collision	Result to B-29	Fighter Casualty
Corp Handa	47 fr	Type 2 (Tojo)	Front side	Tail slighty forward	Damagee	Killed
Sgt Sawamoto	53 fr	Type 2 (Nick)	———	Right inboard engine	Damagee	Killed
1st Lt Shinomiya	244 fr	Type 2 (Tony)	Head on	Near outboard engine	Destroyed	Safe [1]
Corp Itagaki	244 fr	Type 2 (Tony)	Above front side	Unknown	Damaged	Parachuted to safety
Sgt Yoshida	244 fr	Type 2 (Tony)	Above rear	Right inboard engine	Damaged	Killed [2]
2nd Lt Watanabe	53 fr	Type 2 (Nick)	Above front side	Unknown	Damaged	Killed [2]
Maj Hirose	Meiji Air Group	Type 4 (Frank)	Unknown	Empennage	Damaged	Killed [2]
Capt Kawakami	Meiji Air Group	Type 1 (Oscar)	Front	Engine	Destroyed	Killed [2]
Sgt Kuroda & Sgt Takabashi	16 fes	Ki-46 (Dinah)	Below right	Empennage	Damaged	One killed; one parachuted to safety
1st Lt Shiroda	55 fr	Type 3 (Tony)	Unknown	Tail	Destroyed	Killed
1st Lt Urai	55 fr	Type 3 (Tony)	Above front side	Front	Damaged	Killed
Sgt Takamuko	55 fr	Type 3 (Tony)	Above front side	Rudder	Damaged	Safe
Sgt Major Awamura	47 fr	Type 4 (Frank)	Rear	Tail	Damaged	Parachuted to safety
Sgt Koman	47 fr	Type 2 (Tojo)	———	Inboard engine	Damaged	Killed
2nd Lt Tange	244 fr	Type 2 (Tojo)	Rear side	———	Destroyed	Killed
2nd Lt Takayama	244 fr	Type 3 (Tony)	Above rear	Tail	Damaged	Parachuted to safety
2nd Lt Kobayashi	244 fr	Type 3 (Tony)	Above rear	Tail	Damaged	Parachuted to safety

1. Plane lost half of left wing. Landed safely   2. At time of crash, all but fuselage fell off. Because of damage to parachute, pilot died.

Fig J

7. B-29 RAMMING ATTACKS

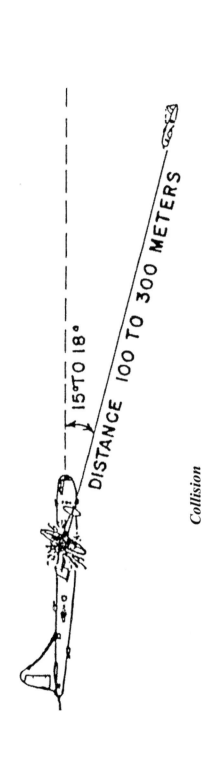

15° TO 18°

DISTANCE 100 TO 300 METERS

Collision

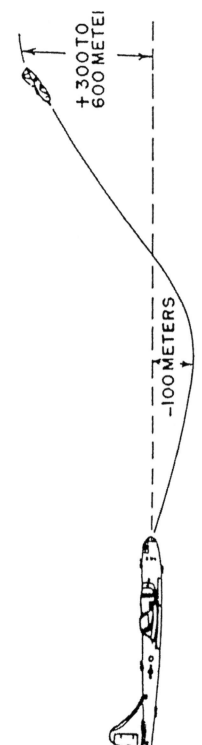

+300 TO 600 METE[]

−100 METERS

Belly Approach from Ahead of Target

pilots regarding the commanders decision as to the best approach. Based upon a study of standard United States Antiaircraft Force formations, specific rules were adhered to in target selection in order to prevent conflict. However, in case a single plane unexpectedly encountered the enemy, the pilot was supposed to attack on his own initiative while maintaining radio contact.

TRAINING

During ground training, pilots were drilled on the importance of a successful collision, and constant efforts were made to instil trainees with patriotism. The course of instruction covered enemy capabilities (especially weak points, formations and tactics), plus a thorough knowledge of the fighter pilot's own limitations. Actual light training in making contact with approaching pseudo attackers was covered in the final phase.

ASSESSMENT OF RESULTS

An examination of figure J discloses that attacks (prior to adoption of the above SOP) resulted in 4 B-29s being destroyed and 13 damaged. It is evident that even these haphazard attacks, which at first glance seem highly inefficient, were in reality very effective. An analysis reveals the following results attained:

- Japanese casualties: Eleven airmen, sixteen fighters destroyed.
- American casualties: Forty airmen; four B-29s destroyed.

These statistics do not take into consideration possible additional bomber crew casualties and the probable extensive damage to the targets not destroyed. It is evident that even with orthodox aircraft, proper instruction could raise the standards of proficiency to a high degree, - especially when employing mass attacks. Although the target value of a B-29 was only a fraction of that of a surface vessel, there was the compensating factor that a pilot could re-attack after a mid-air miss.

Fortunately for the B-29s, the Japanese Air Forces had become relatively impotent by the time the tactical procedure for ramming was being perfected.

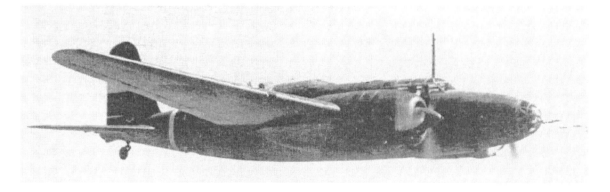

Mitsubishi Ki-21 (Sally) Army Medium Bomber

Nakajima Ki-87 High Altitude Flyer

8. B-29 OPERATIONS

Ki-45 Type 2 Toryu Dragon Slayer (Nick) Army Fighter

GENERAL

During the 9 months of Twentieth Air Force B-29 operations, the fighter opposition never began to approach the intensity of that offered by the Luftwaffe. Furthermore the effectiveness was greatly diminished because of the Japanese interceptor's poor high-altitude performance and lack of heavy armament.

B-29 OPERATIONS

The B-29 missions may be divided into three categories:

- High altitude precision daylight missions (24 November 1944 to 25 February 1945). The bombing programme of this period limited B-29s range and target selection. Therefore the Japanese were able to concentrate their fighters in their defence of these few areas. Throughout this phase, relatively small B-29 forces met their most intense opposition from Japanese interception which showed continual improvement.
- Low and medium daylight missions (25 February to 11 August 1945) The lower bombing altitude, which increased the. B-29 range was coupled with. the employment of far greater numbers of B-29's Japanese were no longer able to concentrate their fighters at a few points. The diversion of the Japanese Air Force" to the Okinawa campaign, and the employment of B-29 fighter escort further contributed to greatly diminishing Jap fighter attacks.
- Night missions. On 9 March, during the period of un-aggressive Japanese fighter activity night missions were initiated by a force of almost 300 B-29s. Some more effective Japanese night fighter armament was employed, but the Japanese performance was still below par and handicapped by the increased difficulty of locating and maintaining contact with the B-29s

JAPANESE DAYLIGHT FIGHTER TACTICS (CONVENTIONAL ARMAMENT)

Attacking out of the sun or clouds was considered relatively unimportant to the Japs in view of their final tendency to standardise on two combat proven tactics. Both these tactics were extremely difficult for flexible gunners to counter, and embodied maximum incorporation of the surprise element.

Straggling members of a loose bomber formation, and isolated B-29s were given first priority on targets. This procedure usually eliminated opposition from heavy defensive formation fire power. Nevertheless, even when attacking a close formation, the surprise element of the frontal attack often precluded an efficient defence.

B-29 WEAKNESSES

The importance and necessity of harmonising the ventral fire-control system was given only secondary consideration by the groups and wings because of operational demands on the aircraft, and greatly decreased fighter opposition. The overall consequence was that the majority of central fire control systems were always improperly harmonised; thereby ,countering to a great degree, the B-29 principal gunnery feature.

The human-surprise element coupled with a slow fire control computer reaction nullified most opposition to the frontal attack.

The B-29 crews, assuming the inability of Jap night fighters to locate them, adopted a passive role and gunners were instructed not to open fire unless fired upon. This procedure resulted in greater comparative safety for the Japanese, especially in view of the Japanese oblique gun installation and the B-29s night silhouette vulnerability. The night flying B-29B, being equipped with only tail armament, was totally unable to oppose the Japanese oblique gun attacks due to the lack of belly defences. This lightly armed model B was used to supplement the standard B-29 during night attacks. The B-29 was unable to produce any "super" fire power against fighter attacks by the orthodox Japanese day fighter.

Conventional Fighter Tactics Against the B-29

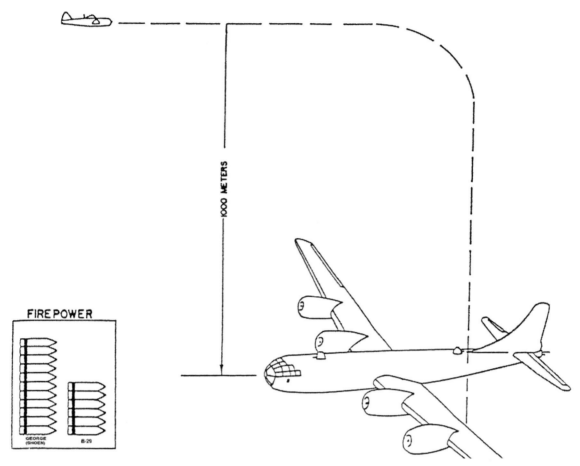

Frontal Overhead Attack

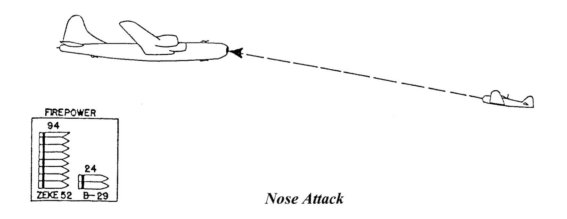

Nose Attack

Fig L

HEAVY BOMBER DEFENCE REQUIREMENTS

A single B-29 could not hold its own in fire power in 1945 against a lone Jap fighter; but a further fire power comparison with the more superior FW 190 or Me 262 emphasizes this defensive weakness.

In addition to the present B-29 all angle turret coverage, heavier fire power is immediately essential in the following sectors, and with the following priority. First, tail, second, belly, third nose. The heaviest fire power is required in the tail sector not only in view of the tendency for all attacks to finish up in this zone, but because of the simpler flying and sighting problems offered the attacking fighter. The under defences are next in importance due to the night silhouette vulnerability from below and the possibility of a simple no deflection shot from upward-firing oblique guns. The zone next in importance is the nose, due to the major surprise element. However, the attackers' interception and flying problems are amplified due to the high rate of closure, and such attacks become less practicable with the present increases in air speeds.

The overhead and beam sectors are least vulnerable. Maximum altitudes complicate overhead attacks; and pursuit attacks from these angles will wind up in the tail plane. Parallel oblique gun attacks from the beam or above are less simple and not as practicable as belly attacks.

The tail sector of the heavy bomber is most urgently in need of increased fire power. The minimum total fire power output should be at least equivalent to the heaviest-armed fighters of World War 11 (the most efficient aircraft cannon of the war, the German Mk 108 is now in the hands of all major powers and it is not unlikely that guns in this category will be used during the initiation of any conflict in the near future) The vulnerability of American bombers to the Mk-108 has been clearly demonstrated in the European theatre, therefore this firepower increase is required for the immediate future, possibly by the modification of existing installations. It should be noted that even the early inferior Japanese fighter fire power output rapidly arose to a point in 1945 where it exceeded United States aircraft fire power. Although it was not until late in the war that the Japanese were able to surpass the fire power of our heavy bombers tail defences, it must be remembered that the Luftwaffe succeeded in doing this two years earlier, in 1943; and even the lightly armed Japanese was earlier able to exceed our fire power defence by selection of angle of attack. The Sam (Reppu) formerly a carrier-based fighter armed with four 20mm cannon was later experimentally remodelled along interceptor lines with six guns of 30 mm calibre.

The theory of bomber formation fire-power implies that fire power will be multiplied by inter aircraft support fire against an attacker. However, in actual practice the inevitable straggling bomber and the adoption of defence-saturating mass fighter tactics nullified this theoretical advantage, and often resulted in one bomber versus one or more fighters.

The accuracy of a gyro stabilised automatic computing gun sight, and radar ranging and tracking are essential to good day and night fire control.

Future trends will undoubtedly necessitate further changes in bomber defence. The additional airspeed and higher altitude will materially decrease the bombers vulnerability and possibly preclude most nose attacks. However, with the advent of guided missiles (including piloted, remotely controlled, and homing types) the tail sector will remain increasingly vulnerable to attack. The potentially smaller size and lower vulnerability of guided missiles will increase the need for more effective tail defence and necessitate revolutionary counter weapons.

Mitsubishi J2M Raiden (Jack) Navy Fighter

Two Ki-27b models bearing the badge of the Akeno Fighter Training School
Most WW2 Army fighter pilots trained on Ki-27s

Mitsubishi A7M Reppu (Sam) Navy Fighter

9. AIRCRAFT ARMAMENT

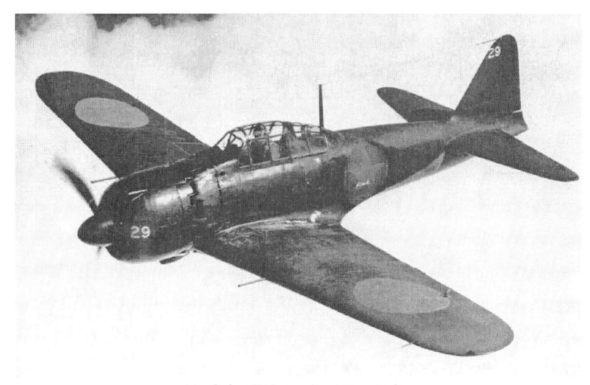

Mitsubishi A6M Reisen (Zero) Navy Fighter

GENERAL

The study of Japanese aircraft armament reveals a drastic failure on their part to standardise on anyone particular weapon for each calibre size. The separate development projects carried out by the two services, Army and Navy, have produced an unsurpassed variety of weapons requiring various types of ammunition.

A parallel comparison of American and Japanese machine guns and ammunition types reveals the great extent of this failure to standardise (Figures M and N)

EXPLANATORY NOTES: AIRCRAFT MACHINE GUNS

Type 89

This weapon is a development of a light machine gun used by the ground forces. There were two distinct types: the single *fed* by a flat drum magazine; and the dual, consisting of a right and left hand gun mounted on a light tubular frame and *fed* by two quadrant-shaped magazines.

Type 89A

The mechanism of these weapons is basically the same. However, though the calibres are both 7.7 mm, be used in the other. The Navy Type 97 uses rimmed ammunition and the Army Type 98 uses a semi-rimmed cartridge.

Type 92

The Navy 7.7 mm guns are chambered to fire the British :303 ammunition, and are almost exact copies of British models. Limited quantities of captured British ammunition were used.

Type 97

Despite the identical calibre and common mechanism, no attempt was made to standardise these guns, and the components were not considered interchangeable This is a twin-mounted gun, and is sometimes designated the Type 100.

Type 1 Browning

These guns both bear a very close resemblance to the United States calibre .50 Browning, but none of the ammunition is interchangeable

Type 2 Mauser

This gun is a very close copy of the German Mg-131. The ammunition is similar to that used by the Germans, but, due to difficulty in perfecting the Luftwaffe's highly efficient electrical synchronisation, the standard percussion type primer was employed.

HO-I, HO-3

The prototype of these guns 20mm Type 97 anti tank rifle. Ammunition is the same for both types but the magazines are not interchangeable.

MG 151/20

This weapon was imported in large quantities from Germany and has been found only with German--manufactured ammunition.

HO-5

This gun is an enlarged model of the US calibre .50 Browning, and was the first 20mm gun capable of synchronised fire produced by the Japanese. (The United States 20mm aircraft gun was not capable of synchronisation).

Type 99

There were three models of the Mark One version and all fired the same ammunition. The Mark Two was later designed in order to increase the muzzle velocity; this new ammunition had a longer cartridge case but contained the same projectile.

DEVELOPMENT 7940-45

Up until 1940 research and development was centred in the rifle calibre class (7.7mm). Aircraft guns were principally limited to adaptations of existing British weapons (Vickers, Lewis and Bren) with the Navy going as far as to adopt the .303 British ammunition.

Operational Machine Guns

Caliber class	United States Air Forces: Army and Navy	Japanese Air Forces: Army or Navy
.30 inch	Cal .30 Browning	Cal .7.7 millimetre type 89 Japanese A. Cal .7.7 millimetre type 89 Vickers A. Cal .7.7 millimetre type 92 Lewis N. Cal .7.7 millimetre type 97 Vickers N. Cal .7.92 millimetre type 1 Dreyse-Solothurn MG15N. Cal .7.92 millimetre type 98 Dreyse-Solothurn MG15A Cal .7.92 millimetre type 1 Bren A
.50 inch	Cal .50 Browning	Cal .12.7 millimetre HO 103 type 1 Browning A. Cal .13 millimetre type 2 Mauser MG-131 N. Cal .13.2 millimetre type 3 Browning N.
20 millimeters	Cal .20 millimetre Hispano-Suiza	Cal .20 millimetre HP-1 and 3 Japanese A. Cal .20 millimetre Mauser MG-150/20 A. Cal .20 millimetre HO-5 Browning A. Cal .20 millimetre type 99 Oerlikon MK-I N. Cal .20 millimetre type 99 Oerlikon MK-II N.

Aircraft Machine Gun Ammunition Operational Types

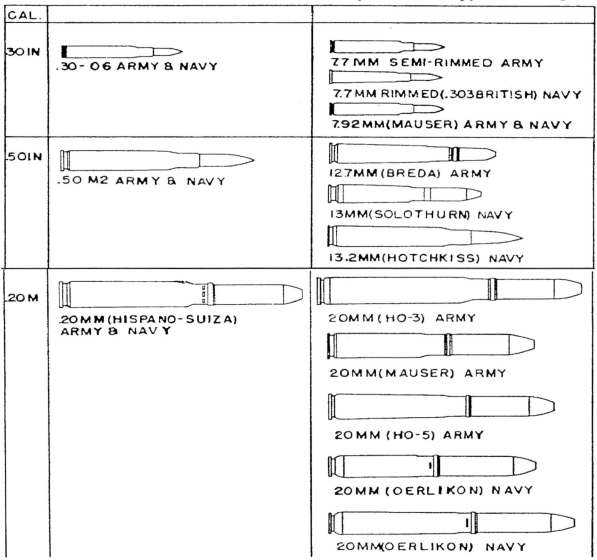

In 1942 production was under way by both the Army and Navy on copies of the Rheinmetall 7.92mm gun (German Mg-15) following the receipt of specimens purchased from. Germany.

As early as 1937, 20mm guns were being manufactured under the guidance of the Oerlikon Company. Three years later, in 1940, the superiority of this calibre was revealed when they were used as wing guns on the Zero fighter over Hawnkow, during the China Incident. Despite this early operational trial, it was not until late in 1944 that guns in the 20 mm or even the calibre .50 were installed for all-round operational use. This delay can be attributed to the insistence of many pilots to have. wing guns removed in order to retain their only 'performance advantages: manoueverability and climbing speed. Furthermore, the continued unreliability of the Japanese synchronisation system prohibited efficient fuselage installations.

After ground firing tests with numerous types, including a trial 25mm gun, vulnerability estimates brought forth the sound conclusion that a gun of at least 30mm was required for an effective percentage of heavy bomber kills. Late in 1943, this theory was verified in combat by a few Zeros equipped with 30mm wing guns) which went into action at Rabaul. With the growing emphasis on the anti-bomber tactics, plans were. initiated to develop more efficient types in the heavier 30mm, 37mm and 40mm categories. (Under this programme the Navy designed the original and efficient Type 5, 30mm; and the Army the revolutionary Ho-30 1, 40mm), Upon hearing of the German antibomber successes, steps were taken to purchase quantities of the highly superior Mk-108 30mm and ammunition. However, the German submarines transferring this material were captured or sunk, and all that ever reached the Japanese Air Forces were two specimens.

During the last year of the war, an attempt was made to' follow the steps of the pioneering Luftwaffe, and efforts were applied toward the development of a gun capable of downing a bomber with a single hit. In view of the increasing urgency for standardisation, a belated decision was made to have the Army handle all designing for cannon in this category. The following experimental models were undergoing development when the war ended:
1. Ho-251, 47 millimetres.
2. Ho-401, 57 millimetres
3. Ho0402, 57 millimetres
4. Ho-501, 70 millimetres
5. Ho-50S, 75 millimetres
6. Ho-600, 120 millimetres

NOTEWORTHY DEVELOPMENTS
The "MA" projectile - The Army developed a very efficient, fuzeless, high explosive incendiary projectile. This ammunition was so simple in design, and proved so efficient in gas tank and fuselage ignition, that it was undergoing adoption by the Navy. The research and development programme formulated five calibres in the following sequence:
1. 7.7 mm (Ma-1O1)
2, 12.7mm (Ma-102) for use against B-17s and B-29s
3. 20mm (Ma-202) for use against 'B-17s and B-29s
4. 37mm (Ma-351) for use against B-29s
5. 30mm (Ma-301) for general anti-bomber use.
It is interesting to note that complete specimens of American bombers were unavailable in Japan in September 1943, during the Ma ammunition firing tests. In view of this the

Army technical laboratory undertook the construction *of* full-size models of B-17s and B-24s exactly to United States specifications. (Tests with the 13mm Ma against the B-17 model disclosed great difficulty in effecting penetration of wing tanks directly from above as opposed to easy penetration from front or rear) Resultant Japanese theoretical estimates *of* hits required to down a heavy bomber (B-17 or B-24) were as follows:
Ground test results:
Ma- 102 (l3mm) 5-6 rounds 20
Ma-202 (20mm) 2-3 rounds 10

Due to the fact that the non-vulnerable target areas were not given full consideration (the incendiary effect was generally limited to gas tanks) coupled with the lack *of* accurate combat assessments (the Japanese did not carry gun cameras in operations) the estimate was somewhat optimistic. Nevertheless, in the Ma the Japanese had an efficient fuzeless projectile, simple to manufacture, and with excellent incendiary properties.

The Ho-301: 40mm cannon.
This revolutionary Japanese development showed great promise. The ammunition for this cannon is of a type not previously used in automatic weapons. The propelling charge is contained in a cavity in the rear of the projectile and therefore no cartridge case is required. The entire cartridge assembly, including the ordinary percussion-type primer is fired from the muzzle. Twelve exhaust ports in the base plate permit the expanding gases to escape and drive the projectile forward. However, this is definitely not a rocket, as the quick-burning propellant is consumed before leaving the barrel. (Figure U)

The comparatively low velocity of 220 metres per second (722 ft per second) was no great handicap in the light of current antibomber tactics. The cannon was similar to the orthodox Oerlikon design, but was a very light weapon for its calibre, weighing only 40 kg (88lbs). The unusual type of ammunition permitted simple gun construction and efficient operation in view of the following advantages.

The weight of one round was relatively light (only slightly above that of the 30mm Ho-155) and of comparatively small dimensions. This permitted carrying a large number of rounds per gun.

The problems of extraction and ejection of empty cases was entirely eliminated. This not only permitted a simpler mechanism but, furthermore, showed promise of development into extremely high rates of fire.

Aichi E16A (Paul) Navy Reconnaissance

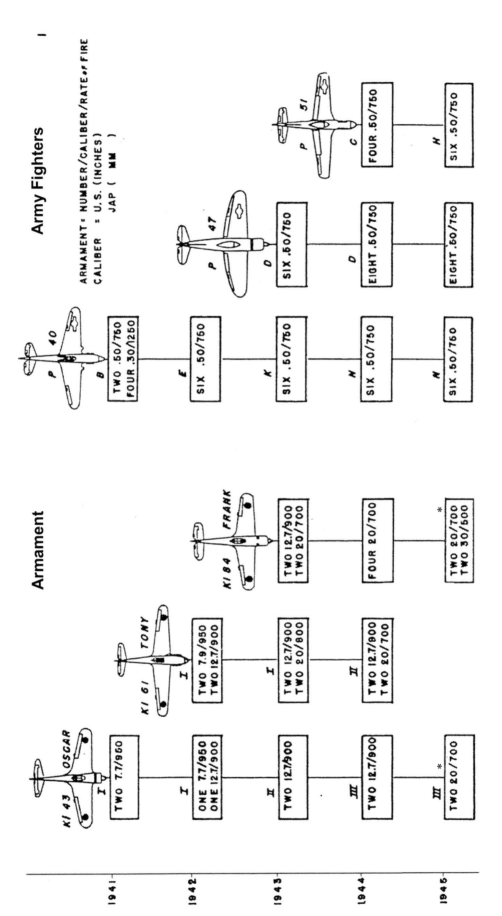

Army Fighters

ARMAMENT= NUMBER/CALIBER/RATE,.FIRE
CALIBER = U.S. (INCHES)
          JAP (MM)

Armament

* - Limited Operational Use (Experimental Installation)

Fig Q.

47.

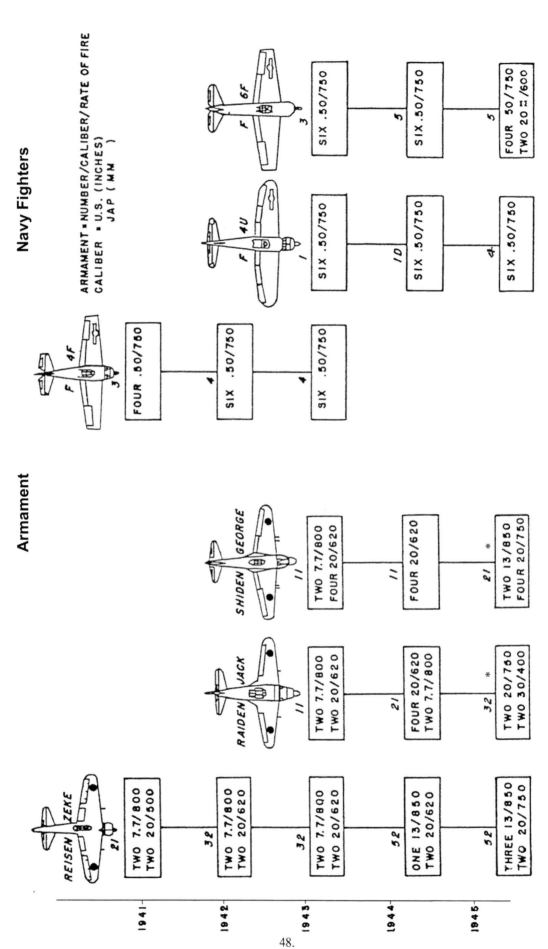

Navy Fighters

Armament

ARMAMENT = NUMBER/CALIBER/RATE OF FIRE
CALIBER = U.S. (INCHES)
         JAP (MM)

F 6F

3	SIX .50/750
5	SIX .50/750
5	FOUR 50/750 TWO 20 ≈/600

F 4U

I	SIX .50/750
ID	SIX .50/750
4	SIX .50/750

F 4F

3	FOUR .50/750
4	SIX .50/750
4	SIX .50/750

SHIDEN GEORGE

II	TWO 7.7/800 FOUR 20/620
II	FOUR 20/620
2I *	TWO 13/850 FOUR 20/750

RAIDEN JACK

II	TWO 7.7/800 TWO 20/620
2I	FOUR 20/620 TWO 7.7/800
32 *	TWO 20/750 TWO 30/400

REISEN ZEKE

2I	TWO 7.7/800 TWO 20/500
32	TWO 7.7/800 TWO 20/620
32	TWO 7.7/800 TWO 20/620
52	ONE 13/850 TWO 20/620
52	THREE 13/850 TWO 20/750

1941   1942   1943   1944   1945

* - Limited Operational Use (Experimental Installation)

Fig R.

48.

Comparative Changes in Fighters' Firepower—U.S. and Japanese

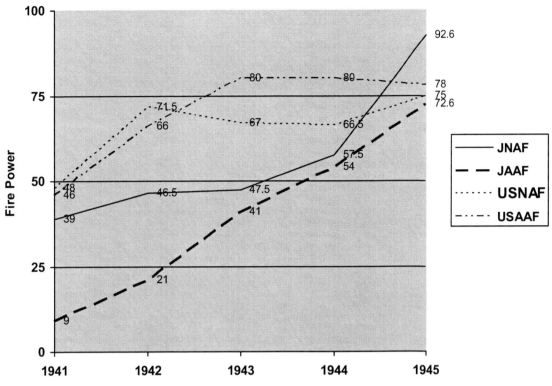

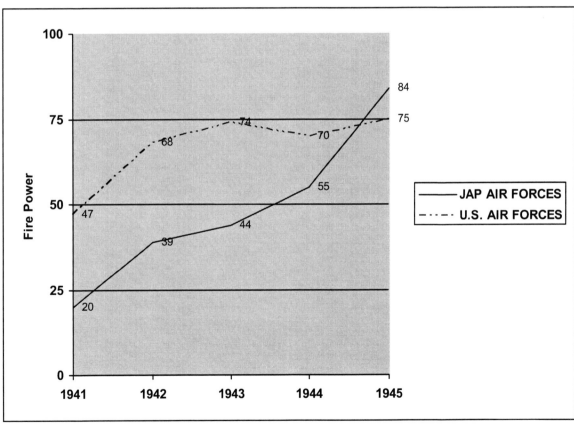

Fire-Power = destruction coefficient x No. of guns x RDS per second
(Ref: "Armament in the air War" USSBS ETO)

Fig S.

Comparative Changes in Fighter Horsepower—U.S. and Japanese
(Sea Level Averages)

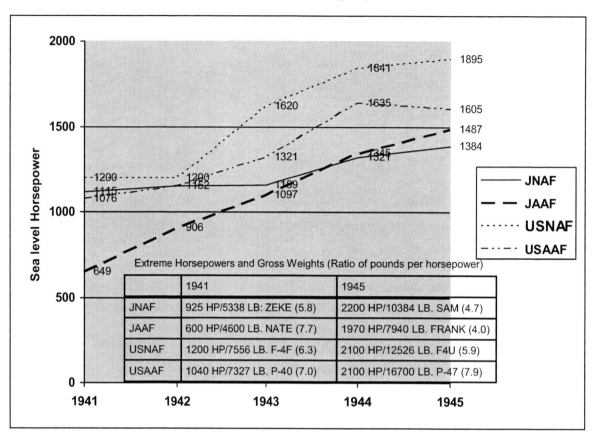

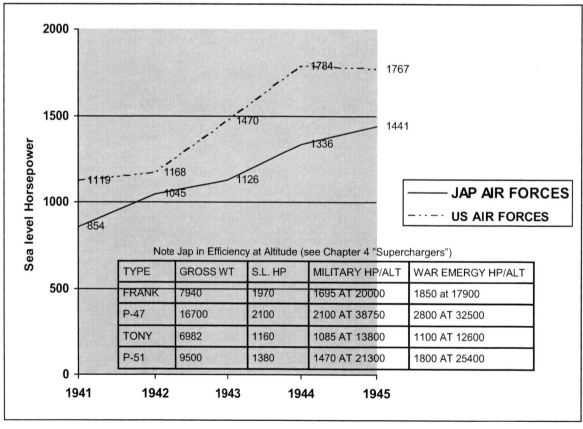

Fig T.

HO-301 40MM H.E.

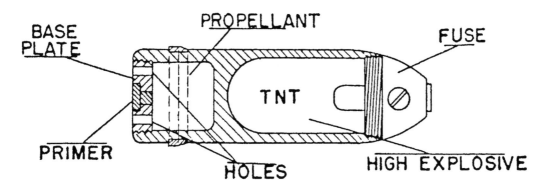

IN THE HO-301 CANNON THE HEAD OF THE
BOLT IS MACHINED AS A PISTON WHICH CLOSES
THE BREECH UPON THE FORWARD STROKE.

"MA" Fuseless H.E./I

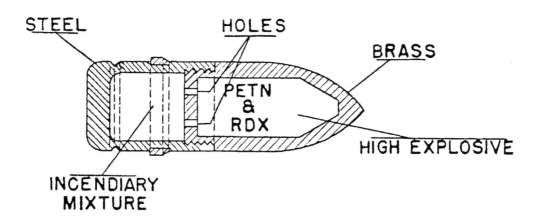

THE FUSELESS MA WAS PRODUCED IN
THE FOLLOWING CALIBERS.

    7.7 MM (MA 101)
    12.7 MM (MA 102)
    20.0 MM (MA202)
    30.0 MM (MA 301)
    37.0 MM (MA 351)

Fig U.

Kawasaki Ki-96 Army Fighter

10. SPECIAL ARMAMENT INSTALLATIONS

Mitsubishi Ki-83 Army Fighter

GENERAL

Paralleling the successful Luftwaffe practice, both the Army and Navy fighters made operational use of the highly advantageous inclined-fixed guns. Though not reaching the scientific perfection of the German "magic eye" automatic firing weapons, the Nipponese added' variety to the installations and broadened the tactical application. Though principally used on night fighters, these offset guns neutralised the value of United, States flexible gunnery methods (position" firing) as well as the automatic compensation of the K-13 variety of gun sight. Army installations were restricted to the upward--firing type, and, in this category, both Army and Navy gave preference to a 30 degree fore-upward angle, supplemented by a few 70 degree installations

ARMY INSTALLATIONS

Ki-45. Two 30, degree upward inclined Ho-5 20R'lm guns, in addition to the following standard mounts; one Ho-203 37mm cannon in fuselage and one type 98 7.92mm dorsal mount (first employed in September 1943)

Ki-46. One 70 degree upward inclined Ho-204 37mm cannon. (Although originally planned as a reconnaissance type, this proved to have such superior high-altitude performance that in August 1944 it was converted to a fighter pending the appearance of a true high- altitude fighter).

Same as above in addition to the two standard fuselage-mounted guns, Ho-5 20mm (1945)

Ki-84. Three upward inclined Ho-5 20 mm guns in addition to the two standard mounted Ho-5's in the wings (experimental 1945)

Ki-102. Two upward inclined Ho-5 20mm guns, in addition to the two standard fuselage mounted Ho-155 30 mm cannon.

NAVY INSTALLATIONS

Gekko (Irving 11) Fighter. Two upward inclined plus two 30 degrees downward inclined type 99 20 mm guns.

Ginka (Frances) Four type 99 20mm forward firing guns inclined upwards at 30 degrees.

Seventeen type 99 20mm guns in the bomb bay; 12 firing forward; 5 rearward, and all downward at an inclined angle

Twelve type 99 20mm guns in bomb bay, inclined forward to fire in a concentrated cone (experimental)

Raiden (Jack 32) Two type 99 20mm guns inclined fore--upwards, in addition to the- two standard 7.7mm wing guns.

Susei (Judy 12) One type 99 20 mm gun inclined fore--upwards, in addition to the two standard 7.7mm wing guns

Reisen (Zeke) One type 99 20mm gun inclined at 30 degrees fore-upwards, in addition to the two standard 20mm wing guns.

Tenrai Two type 99 20mm guns, plus two type 2 13mm guns, all inclined fore-upwards (1945)

TACTICS

Antibomber - The Gekko was used operationally with upward, downward and sideward guns, but battle experience proved that the upward-firing installations were the most effective. The Gekko was successfully employed against 8-29s and heavy bombers (Figure V). Future plans were centred on wider use of the 30mm machine cannon in inclined mounts.

Aerodrome attacks - Thirty Ginkas with the 17 20mm guns in downward inclined installations, were in preparation to be staged through Minami to attack 8-29 bases in the Marianas and thence to land at;Truk. The Navy believed that one pass could wipe out all the 829s arranged alongside the runway, but the untimely temination of the war put an end to this scheme.

Anti-landing craft - The Ginka with the 12 gun downward installation was designed to discharge

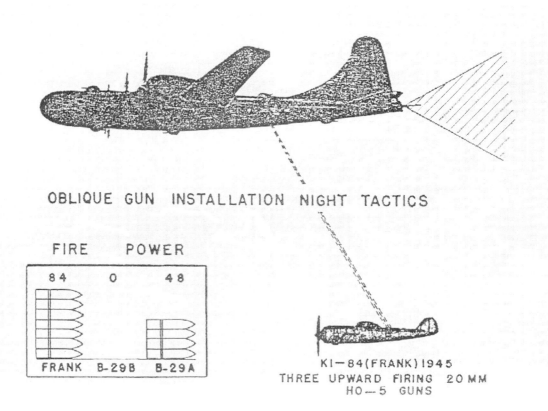

OBLIQUE GUN INSTALLATION NIGHT TACTICS

FIRE POWER

84	0	48
FRANK	B-29B	B-29A

KI—84 (FRANK) 1945
THREE UPWARD FIRING 20 MM
HO—5 GUNS

Night Fighter Tactics

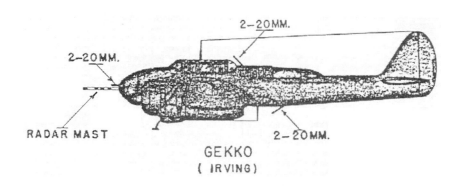

2—20MM.

2—20MM.

RADAR MAST

2—20MM.

GEKKO
(IRVING)

Fig V.

Yokosuka D4Y-3 Suisei (Judy) Navy Attack Aircraft

11. AIR TO AIR BOMBING

Nakajima B6N Tenzan (Jill) Navy Attack Aircraft

AIR- TO-AIR BOMBING

Much attention was directed toward air-to-air technique, including free falling bombs, cable bombs, and parachute bombs. These very extensive developments were, however, limited in operational use by the poor high-altitude performance of Japanese aircraft.

Theory of free air-to-air bombing. Research in 1941 by General Masaki resulted in the following sound conclusions.

1. Only the parallel course approach would be effective when attacking single aircraft or small units.
2. Frontal attacks must be limited in use to large formations.
3. Oblique attacks would be relatively inaccurate.
4. The choice of time or impact fuze would depend primarily on:
    (a) Probable error in time of the time fuze; ,
    (b) Effective radius of bomb burst.

Ordinary demolition bomb with time fuze.
In 1942 and 1943 the time ,fuzed demolition bomb was used experimentally. This was employed in a manner similar to the basic Luftwaffe operational technique; whereby the fighter flew a parallel course, and released the single bomb from a height corresponding to the time-fuze setting.

Multiple scattering bombs (Figure W) The first Army developments in multiple air--to-air missiles were the scattering "baby bombs" which were produced experimentally in 1941 and 1942. The To-3 was primarily for aerial targets, but the principal purpose of other small grenade like objects was to destroy parked aircraft in attacks on airfields. These could be scattered in clusters of 30 to 40, or individually released in train from auxiliary bomb' racks carried under the wings. The To-3 clustered together nose-to-tail in such manner that the arming vane could revolve only after break-up of the cluster.

Evolving from the scattering bomb, the Ta bomb was developed for use against aerial targets. The Ta was a 40mm hollow charge streamlined bomb weighing one-third of a kilogram (0.74lb). These missiles were released over bombers, in clusters of 30 or 76 (30 and 50 kg (66 and 110 lbs) cluster weight. Japanese Army reports indicate that these bombs brought down several US Antiaircraft heavy bombers in the South Pacific; being especially effective against large close formations.

From a theoretical standpoint the tail attack should prove most effective in employing the Ta bomb. However, fighters were reluctant to approach too close to the tail defences without a 1000 metre (3281 ft) advantage in altitude, and such a procedure without a special sight would be futile. The Ta was therefore first used operationally in 1943, with a frontal diving attack employed in view of the lessened danger to the attacking fighter.

The frontal diving attack procedure is illustrated in Figure X, The success of this technique was based on a set of tables; pre-calculated "direct aiming" angles for various altitudes and target speeds. A gun sight was used and the bomb was released at a height H from the release angle MTC. If MTC was the "direct aiming" angle given in the bombing tables, then the time of fall MBC was equal to the time of flight of distance TC, and the bomb will hit the target. If the pilot found difficulty in realising the "direct aiming" angle, he could make last minute adjustments by using a supplementary correction table.

An alternate method of employing a front horizontal attack was suggested (Figure X). Here the fighter needed only to adjust his relative height. The bomb was released when the target wing span filled a preset reticle width. However, the desire of the fighter to retain freedom of manoeuvre precluded the use of this simple method.

Just prior to the armistice, experimental employment of oblique tail attacks were begun against B-29s. This technique remained unperfected when the war ended. .

The Navy counterpart of the Ta bomb was a heavier, 1 kg (2205lbs) hollow-charge baby bomb, the Type 2 No 6 Mk-21 model I, which was released in clusters of 40. Like the Army Ta, it had an aerial. burst fuze which opened the container shortly after release. The hollow-charge, armour-piercing nose, was later considered by the Navy as superfluous against aircraft, and was soon superceeded by a more streamlined type which had a solid black powder nose charge.

The final standard, model 2 housed 36 bombs and weighed a total of 49kg (108lbs)

Ro-Ta grenade rocket. To eliminate the need for essential superior altitude on the part of the attacker when employing the Ta bomb, the Ro- Ta was developed in 1945. In this weapon 38 Ta bombs were propelled into the formation, in a rocket accelerated container. The forward portion of the Ro- Ta contained the Ta bombs plus a time-fuzed explosion charge which scattered the bombs. Superior height was no longer needed by the attacking fighter who could now fire from a level or low position into the bomber stream. The termination of the war, however, precluded the final development of this excellent weapon.

The Ta-l05. As numerous large American. ships had been damaged by Kamikaze attack, it was believed that the next landing (expected at Kyushu or Honshu) the Allies would employ larger numbers of smaller landing craft. To counter such tactics, the Ta-105, a 100mm version of the original Ta bomb was developed.

The bomb container housed 21 of these Ta-l05's. Like the smaller Ta, the outer case opened after release from the aircraft and the baby bombs scattered. Aside from the variation in dimension, the type 105 differed principally from the original Ta in having large folding tail vanes. The Ta-lOSs hollow charge would be effective against both armoured landing craft and tanks, as it was capable of perforating a steel plate 140mm thick.

Incendiary air-to-air bombs. (Figure Z) In contrast to the Army's specialising exclusively in the high explosive variety of bomb in operations against Allied heavy bombers, the Navy concentrated almost solely on the incendiary type. The mysterious "Balls of' Fire" phenomenon was the explosion of the Navy's aerial burst incendiary shrapnel bomb, known to the Japs as the Sango, but later nicknamed the "Fireball" because of the American newspaper accounts. There were three sizes, 32kg (70.6lbs), 53kg (117lbs) and 250kg (55lbs), but the one most commonly used against the B-29s was the 32 kg (70.6lbs) model m, designated No 3 of the type 99 Mr-3 variety. This bomb carried a bursting charge of shimose (picrid acid) and 198 phosphorus-filled steel pellets. The bomb was built with bent tail fins to impart a spin and increase the accuracy.

PARACHUTE BOMBING
In 1935 the To-2 parachute bomb was developed for anti bomber use, and in 1937 Captain Saito (pilot) developed the tactics illustrated in Figure Y.

The To-2 was a 1.8kg (4lb) bomb, usually carried in clusters of 10. After release, each bomb freed its individual silk parachute from which it became suspended by a steel cable. For greater depth, 2 sizes of parachutes were used, in order to give 2 rates of falling speed. The total weight of one 10 bomb cluster was only 50kg (110lbs) thereby allowing as many as 40 bombs 'to be carried by a single engine fighter. Dropped in the path of a bomber formation, the probability of a strike was good, and a single hit was capable of downing a heavy bomber. The bomber, upon striking the cable, caused the bomb to swing under the aircraft and explode upon impact of the "all-ways" fuze. Direct hits though less remote would, of course, give instantaneous detonation

In Saito's recommended procedure the lead fighters continue straight ahead while the wing aircraft fly off to the beam, all dropping their To bombs in the path of the bombers.

This was potentially an excellent weapon, but three reasons precluded its standardisation:
The bomb suspension cable, developed in 1937 when aircraft had relatively low speeds would sever upon contact with modern aircraft. Further To-2 development was stymied by the great repute of the Ta bomb. Japanese high-altitude performance was still below par.

CABLE BOMBING
The proposed Japanese anti-aircraft force tactics for cable bombing were not unlike the Luftwaffe's operational trials, in that the demolition charge was similarly suspended from a 1,000 metre (3281 ft) long steel cable and dragged through the bomber formation. In both cases the impact-fuzed bomb was lowered by a high-altitude fighter upon approaching the bomber stream, and the attacker's altitude rendered him comparatively immune from the bomber defences. However, instead of the German system of using standard heavy demolition bombs, the Japanese employed a pair of especially designed light-weight bombs incorporating a special release apparatus.

Navy "Ta" Bombs

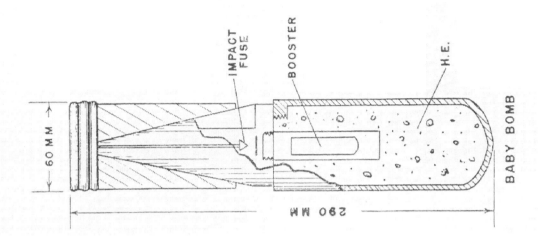

IMPACT FUSE

BOOSTER

H.E.

60 MM

290 MM

BABY BOMB

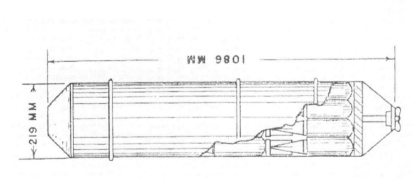

219 MM

1086 MM

60 KG. NO. 21 BOMB
2 STYLE – 2

(CYLINDRICAL CONTAINER
HOUSES 36 BABY BOMBS)

Fig W.

58.

The Germans had early abandoned their cable bombing tactics in view of the increased fighter vulnerability resulting from the very appreciable drag of the heavy demolition bomb. The more highly developed Japanese weapon sidestepped the heavy drag; but nevertheless, did not become operational due to the high altitude requirements exceeding the capabilities of the Jap aircraft.

The Japanese cable bombs were suspended in pairs, one bomb hanging 30 metres (98ft) below the other. The heavier bomb hung at the cable's end, and the bomb weights were 1 kg (2205lbs) and 5 kg (11,025lbs), respectively. The original' purpose of the upper bomb was to cause the bomb load to hang lower and to overcome the tendency to drag directly behind the fighter; the initial prototype of the upper bomb was a 20 cm span inert airfoil for this purpose.

The airfoil finally evolved into the shape illustrated and included an explosive charge. The German heavy demo-type cable bomb' was more destructive, as 100kgs (220.5lbs) to 200kgs (441lbs) of explosive would cause damage within 50 metres (164 feet). However, this demolition advantage was more than overcome by the excessive drag, and was unessential to bomber destruction when incorporating an impact fuze. The Nipponese apparatus was more highly developed and its light bombs were easily capable of destroying a heavy bomber, but, was with most Japanese air-to-air techniques, the lack of a true high-altitude fighter precluded these potentially effective tactics. (German and Japanese cable bombs were apparently developed independently.)

SCARECROW AIR DEFENCES
The attitude of passive bomber defence was further emphasised by the early adoption of defensive scare weapons, arid' reports indicate that these cheap makeshift missiles did have a deterrent effect upon Allied fighers. The following types were in operational use Defensive "Grenade" (Firecracker Type)

This was a waterproofed, pressed paper, spherical container 5.5 ins in diameter. Inside was a black powder burster surrounding flash producing pellets. Thrown by hand from the tail of the bomber, the container burst by friction igniter and the pellets scattered producing flashy low-order explosions.

Defensive parachute "bomb" (non explosive.)
These were small paper parachutes stabilized by inert weights and released by hand from the tail of the aircraft in clusters of 10. Usually about 50 of these small chutes were discharged simultaneously, and the fundamental psychological effect was further enhanced in view of the resemblance to the explosive To-2 parachute bombs.

THE KO-DAN (RUBBER BOMB)
Theory. Much experimental work was put into the "Ko" bomb, a novel rubber-cased demolition bomb believed to have extraordinary destructive power. The theoretical basis of the "Ko" bomb was "Kobayashi's Principle" which follows:

> *The energy of an explosion is projected along lines perpendicular to the surface of the explosive.*
> *The amount of energy developed is proportional to the quantity of explosive within the neutral lines adjacent to the surface.*

Kobayishi based his principle upon observations of ultra high-speed photographs of various shaped explosive charges in process of detonation (Figure BB)

Trials. In the application of this theory it is readily seen that *for* maximum effect we must increase the explosive's area of contact.

The Ko bomb was constructed with a rubber nose connected to a thin, 2mm steel case. Upon impact the rubber nose was flattened, thus producing the larger desired contact area. The Ko was originally designed for employment against heavy concrete emplacements. According to General Masaki, an 85kg bomb (187lbs) (explosive charge = 50kg (110lbs) of 50/50 ultropine and TNT) was capable of penetrating a reinforced concrete slab 1 metre thick with a resultant 1 metre (3281 *feet*) diameter hole; a feat which would ordinarily require a 25Dkg (551lbs) ordinary demolition bomb.

Parachute Bombing Tactics

Air to air "Ta" Bomb Tactics

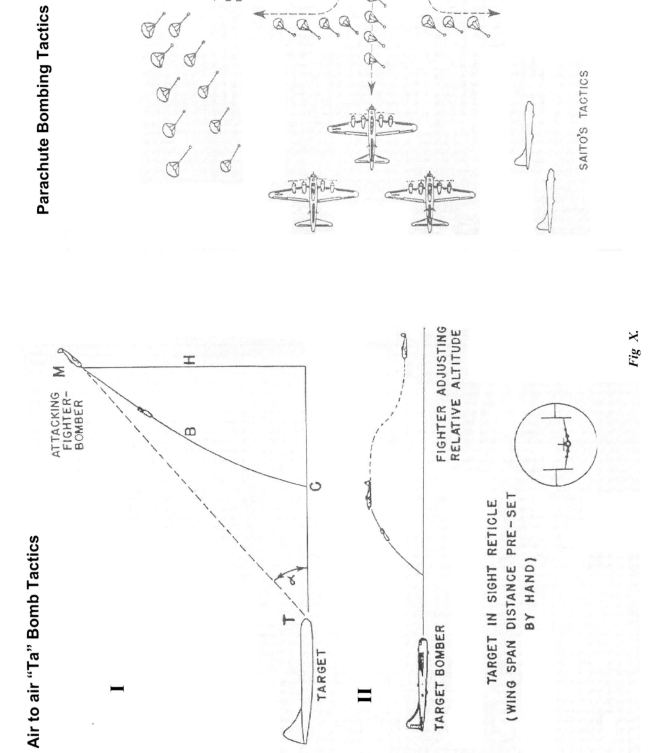

TWO SIZES OF CHUTES IN EACH CLUSTER TO INCREASE DEPTH

SAITO'S TACTICS

Fig Y.

ATTACKING FIGHTER-BOMBER

M

H

B

G

α

T

TARGET

I

II

TARGET BOMBER

FIGHTER ADJUSTING RELATIVE ALTITUDE

TARGET IN SIGHT RETICLE
(WING SPAN DISTANCE PRE-SET BY HAND)

Fig X.

Air to Air Incendiary Bombing

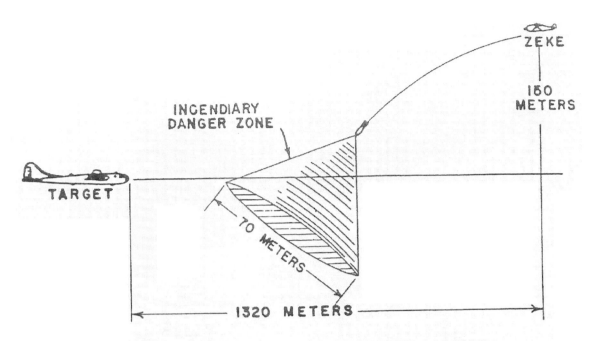

ZEKE

150 METERS

INCENDIARY DANGER ZONE

70 METERS

TARGET

1320 METERS

PHOSPHORUS PELLETS ARE DISPERSED AT A SPEED OF ABOUT 300 METERS PER SECOND

Fig Z1.

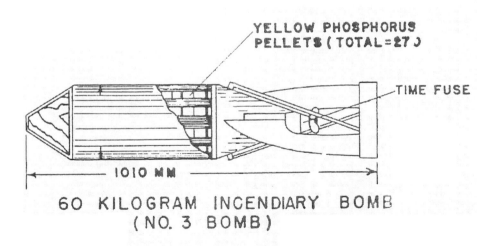

YELLOW PHOSPHORUS PELLETS (TOTAL=27)

TIME FUSE

1010 MM

60 KILOGRAM INCENDIARY BOMB
(NO. 3 BOMB)

60 KG BOMB DESIGNED 1943
IN PRODUCTION SEPT. 1944

Fig Z2.

Air to Air Cable Bombing

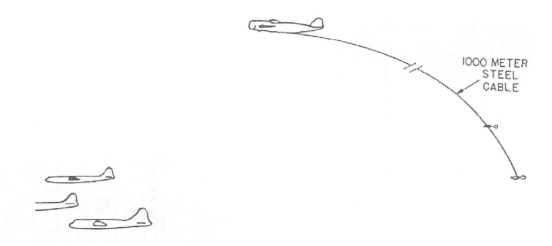

1000 METER STEEL CABLE

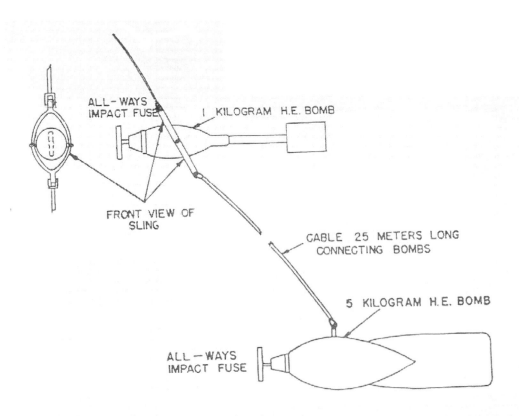

ALL-WAYS IMPACT FUSE

1 KILOGRAM H.E. BOMB

FRONT VIEW OF SLING

CABLE 25 METERS LONG CONNECTING BOMBS

5 KILOGRAM H.E. BOMB

ALL-WAYS IMPACT FUSE

Fig AA.

Ko-Dan Rubber Bomb

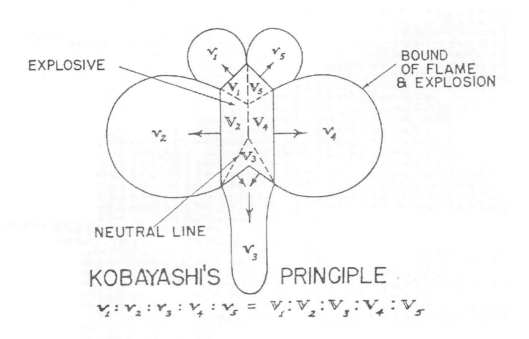

EXPLOSIVE

BOUND
OF FLAME
& EXPLOSION

NEUTRAL LINE

KOBAYASHI'S PRINCIPLE

$$v_1 : v_2 : v_3 : v_4 : v_5 = \mathbb{V}_1 : \mathbb{V}_2 : \mathbb{V}_3 : \mathbb{V}_4 : \mathbb{V}_5$$

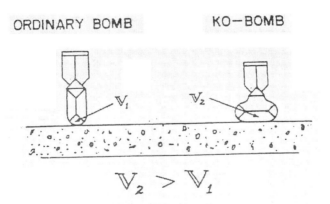

ORDINARY BOMB   KO-BOMB

$$\mathbb{V}_2 > \mathbb{V}_1$$

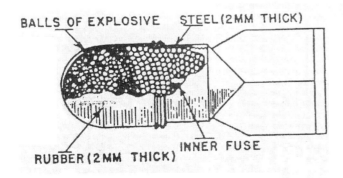

BALLS OF EXPLOSIVE   STEEL (2MM THICK)

RUBBER (2MM THICK)   INNER FUSE

Fig BB.

PHOTOELECTRIC INFLUENCE FUZE

General.
This Japanese fuze (Type 3) was used operationally on 250 and 800 kg (551 and 1764lbs) aircraft bombs to cause detonation 18 to 45 feet above the earth. The fuze functions in daylight or darkness. Operation depends on transmitting from the fuze a beam of pulsating light which is reflected back to the fuze and activates a photoelectric cell, which, in connection with an electric circuit, causes a detonation at a desired height.

Although limited operationally to use against ground targets, this principle promises an excellent solution to the free air-to-air bombing time-fuze problem.

Development and Manufacture.
The principle of the fuze is not new, but the reduction of the idea to a practical and reliable mechanism represents an appreciable achievement which required, amongst other things, the development and manufacture of a new photocell and thyratron tube. An earnest development programme was initiated in November 1943 at the first naval technical arsenal, Kanayawa, and only 9 months later, in July 1944, the fuze was used operationally. The number of fuzes manufactured was said to have been probably less than 1,500.

The main difficulties to be overcome were as follows:
The manufacture of a photocell which did not show "peaks" i.e. a photocell whose current output reliably followed a smooth curve as the light intensity increased.
The manufacture of a thyratron tube which was capable of withstanding the vibration encountered.

Principle of Operation.
As indicated in the diagram (Figure CC) the time of the arming of the fuze may be set before the take-off at any value between 0 and 30 seconds. After arming, the point of detonation is determined principally by how good the target is as a light reflector.

A pulsing light source of 900 to 1000 cycles per second is located In the fuze, and the light from this source is directed. toward the earth during the falling of the bomb. The pulsing light from the bomb strikes this target and is reflected back to a photoelectric cell in the fuze. The current from the photocell is amplified by an electronic circuit, tuned to 900-1000 cycles per second, and connected to a thyratron tube. As the bomb nears the earth, the photoelectric cell receives more and more reflected light so that its current, which is amplified, increases until it triggers the thyratron. When the thyratron triggers, enough current passes through to the detonator to explode the bomb.

Since the amplifying circuit is sensitive only to light, pulsing at 900-1000 cycles per second, a non-pulsating light will not activate the fuze and it may be used in daylight or darkness.
The Type 3 photoelectric influence fuze is about 13 inches high and 10 inches in diameter.

Counter measures
At first thought it might be suggested that a searchlight pulsed at the proper frequency would cause the detonation of this fuze, but it must be realised that the fuze remains insensitive to such light until the arming switch is closed. If the dropping height is known sufficiently accurately when the arming-timer is being set, the period during which the bomb is capable of being activated by a pulse searchlight may be minimised so as to make searchlight detonation impracticable.

Rikugun Ki-93 Army Fighter Two Seater Reconnaissance

Photoelectric Influence Fuse

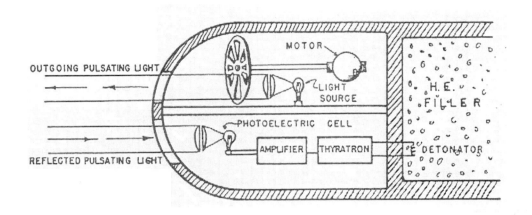

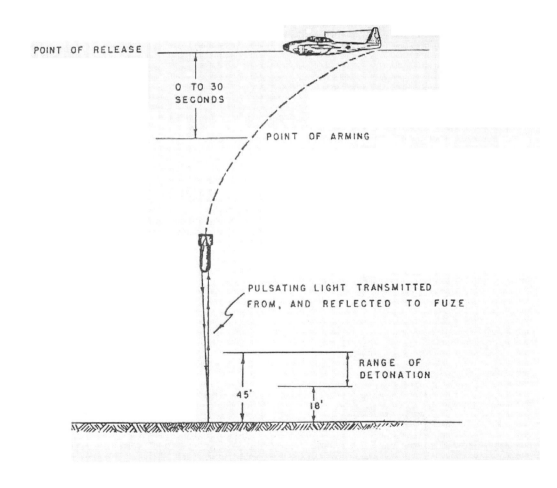

Fig CC.

65.

Aichi B7A Ryusei (Grace) Navy Torpedo Aircraft

12. AIRCRAFT TORPEDOS

Nakajima C6N Saiun (Myrt) Navy Reconnaissance

GENERAL
The Nipponese considered that the torpedo was the most lethal weapon in use against ships, and for the past 20 years the Japanese Navy has conducted an extensive research programme. The result has been the design of torpedoes unrivalled in speed and range, yet carrying an extra weight of explosive. The Jap Type 97 18" midget submarine (oxygen enriched) torpedo carries a larger explosive charge than United States, British or German torpedoes, yet weighs a great deal less, and its speed and range do not. compare too unfavourably with those of the large 21 inch steam torpedoes.

STANDARD AIRCRAFT TORPEDOES
The operational aircraft torpedoes type 91, modifications 1,2 and 3 have a common diameter of 18 inches, with an eight cylinder steam engine. The engine is very well designed and built. It is probably original, and is readily adaptable to large-scale mass production. The disadvantage of the type 91 is its length, which because of its fragility necessitated a somewhat- low dropping height on the part of the Japanese torpedo planes. Type 91 J mod ii. First manufactured in November 1931. Diameter, 45 cm (17.7 ins). velocity 42 knots (48.3 mph) length 5270 mm (17.3 ft). range 2000 metres (2187 yar.cls) explosive charge 150 kg (331 lbs)
This torpedo was used in the Malayan campaign in December 1941; and in the Coral Sea action in May 1942.

Type 91, mod 11. First manufactured in April 1941.
In this model the explosive charge was increased to 205kg (452 lbs)
This torpedo was used at Pearl Harbor and Malaya in December 1941, Coral Sea in May 1942, Midway in June 1942 and in the South Pacific Ocean in August 1942.

Type 91, mod -III. First manufactured in August 1941.
In addition to an explosive charge increase to 240kg -(529lbs) an eight fin tail was fitted which gave improved aerial stabilisation and excellent depth control. The eight fins appear to dampen out vibrations and were quite superior to the former four fin type which gave relatively poor depth performance. The warhead was interchangeable with the following alternate models

Mod III	240 kg (529 lbs)
Mod IV	300 kg (662 lbs)
V head	305 kg (673 lbs)
Kite head	335 kg (730 lbs)
Mod VII	420 kg (926 lbs)

Type 4. This new type was designed to simplify the mass-production and operation. It was built stronger to endure high-speed launching and was put into mass production in December 1944, but never reached th operational stage. Speed 42 knots (48mph), length 5270mm (17.3 ft), range 1500 metres (1641 yards)

COMPARISON OF USN AND JAPANESE AERIAL TORPEDOES
The principal United States Navy advantage of having 4000 yard range was relatively unimportant as the average horizontal range was closer to 1000 yards and seldom exceeded 2000. In the important characteristics of speed and explosive weight the Japanese designs were ahead. The potential launching speeds and altitudes of release were greater with the US Navy torpedo, but the Japanese preference was for the greater hit probability offered by short ranges (which necessitated low speed and low altitudes) with the safety factor given secondary consideration. The type 96 Nell is credited with the sinking of HM ships Prince of Wales and Repulse.
It should be noted that in shallow water launching tactics (40 ft depth) speeds over 297 knots (342mph) and altitudes over 200 ft are unlikely to result in excessive bottom hitting.

TORPEDO BOMBERS
Navy (In order of operational use)

a.   Type 96 land attack plane (Nell)
b.   Type 1 land attack plane (Betty)
c   "Ginka" land-based bomber (Frances)
d.   Type 97 carrier borne bomber (Kate)
e.   Tenzan carrier borne attack plane (Jill)
f.   Ryusei carrier borne attack plane (Grace)

It was hoped that Grace would be adopted as standard to fill all the requirements but considerable problems were met in the tail-control surfaces, although the wind tunnel tests performed satisfactorily. Exhaustive checks eventually found the trouble in the Aichi company jigs; but in the interim many Graces were grounded while modifications were being made. Homare engine troubles also delayed the project. With the need for simplifying the whole aircraft production schedule, it was almost decided to concentrate on Myrt (reconnaissance) as the standard torpedo plane, discarding Grace and Jill for this work.

Army.

Since the Ki-67 bomber (Peggy) was very manoeuvrable and equipped with the necessary electrical apparatus and instruments for night flight, it was tested with torpedo equipment. The results showed satisfactory torpedo release up to the speed range of 550-600k/h (342/373 mph) so this launching apparatus was made standard on all these planes. The first Army torpedo attack took place in the air battle off Taiwan in October 1944.

TORPEDO TACTICS
The standard approach for Japanese Navy torpedo planes was between 3,300 to 10,000 ft depending upon atmospheric and target conditions. When nearing the target ships, especially when within radar range, the planes dropped to 160 feet.

Unless in the face of heavy anti aircraft fire, the aircraft flew in loose string and usually dropped the torpedo from the 160 foot altitude at an air speed from 140 to 160 knots (161 to 184 miles) The release point was 2,600 to 4000 feet in accordance with the final course of the target. (Later in the war, the potential launching speeds tended to increase along with increases in bomber speed; and a late model Japanese torpedo permitted release at speeds up to 600 k/h (373mph)

Torpedo Comparison

	Model	Overall Length inches	Diameter inches	Speed	Range yards	Total Weight pounds	Explosive Weight pounds
United States Navy	Mark XIII	161	22.4	38.6 mph	4,000	2,176	600
	Mod. III	"	"	33.5 knots	"	"	"
Imperial Japanese Navy	Type 91	225	17.7	48.3 mph	3,100	2,100	821
	Mod. VI	"	"	42 knots	"	"	"

Fig DD

Aircraft Torpedo Tactics

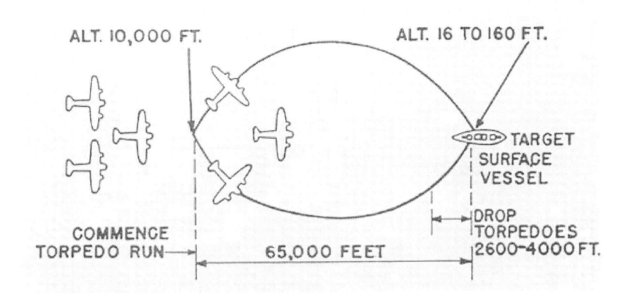

ALT. 10,000 FT.

ALT. 16 TO 160 FT.

TARGET
SURFACE
VESSEL

COMMENCE
TORPEDO RUN

65,000 FEET

DROP
TORPEDOES
2600~4000 FT.

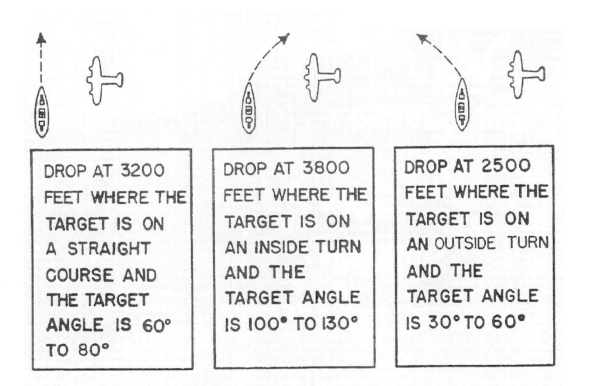

| DROP AT 3200 FEET WHERE THE TARGET IS ON A STRAIGHT COURSE AND THE TARGET ANGLE IS 60° TO 80° | DROP AT 3800 FEET WHERE THE TARGET IS ON AN INSIDE TURN AND THE TARGET ANGLE IS 100° TO 130° | DROP AT 2500 FEET WHERE THE TARGET IS ON AN OUTSIDE TURN AND THE TARGET ANGLE IS 30° TO 60° |

Fig EE

Mitsubishi G4M Navy Bomber

13. ROCKET WEAPONS

Kawasaki Ki-48 (Lilly) Army Light Bomber

DEVELOPMENT

Although the Army and Navy had a rocket information exchange plan in effect since 1943, it was not until March 1944 that there began an attempt of "actual concrete cooperation".

This belated effort was initiated with the decision for the Army to specialise in spin-stablisation and the Army in fin type. (The primary reason for this co-operation was actually the persistence of each air force in adhering to their own beliefs) the idea, and understanding was that should either air fore perfect one of these types, they would both standardise on the perfected weapon.

The Navy's fin-stabilised rocket was the first to show success. The Army, however, protested that the Navy design was based upon the use of naval arsenal production equipment and that Army arsenals could not, be readily adapted to such manufacture. Therefore, development of the Army's spin-stabilised rocket was continued, and eventually
perfected and adopted by their own air force.

OPERATIONAL USE
The Army planned to employ rocket-carrying fighters to combat the Allied landing craft during the Okinawa campaign. However, at this time the spin-rockets. Were still not perfected, and at the war end production had only just begun. Army ground force rockets were late in entering combat; being first encountered in the hills east of Manila. But the Army air force was still longer delayed; never reaching the operational stage.

Kyushu Q1W1 Tokai (Lorna) anti-submarine aircraft

14. GUIDED MISSILES

Kyushu K11W Shiragiku Crew Trainer

GENERAL

Although none of the Japanese non-piloted guided missiles reached the operational stage, the radio controlled I-GO bomb was close to perfection when the war ended. Two other interesting investigations had been undertaken; one regarding a heat-homing bomb and the other a sound-controlled fuze.

THE I-GO BOMB

Following a conference on a new weapons research, held 24 July 1944, it was decided to undertake the design radio controlled flying bomb. The I-GO was released from a parent aircraft at an altitude up to 1500 metres (4922 ft) at a distance of 11 km (6.84 miles) from its objective. It automatically descended to an altitude of 30-150 metres (98.4-492, ft), 5 km (3.18 ft) from the target where a preset altimeter caused it to to level off. After its release I-GO was controlled by radio from a range increasing to 3km (1.86 miles) ahead of the mother plane until the time of impact.

No optical aid was afforded to the bombardier in controlling the flight of the 550 km/h (342 mph) missile, nor was visibility assisted by any flame or smoke emission behind the bomb. However a tail light was added for night employment to aid in keeping the bomb on course. The bombardier had full azimuth and altitude control over the missile, and he put it into a dive just before it got over the target.

Field Tests. The original plan called for two sizes of flying bombs designated the A and B models. The former was to be used against battleships and aircraft carriers and the latter for employment against destroyers and cargo craft.

By the end of October 1944 the first model B was completed by Kawasaki and tested in conjunction with the Ki-48. In the following month the I-GO A constructed by Mitsubishi, was released from the Ki-67 mother plane. Totals of about 15 As and 150 Bs were produced and tested. It was finally decided put all the effort on perfecting the I-GO A because of less electrical trouble and heavier warhead (800kg (1764 Ibs). Both types showed their maximum error in range rather than in azimuth, striking from 30 metres (984 feet) short to 100 metres (328 feet) past the target, possibly due in great part to poor visual judgement

I-GO Bomb and Carrier

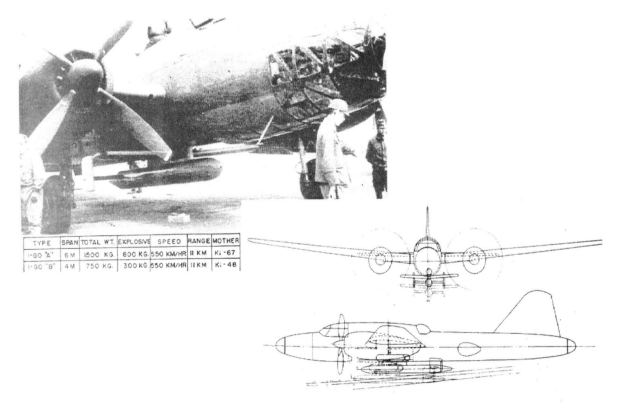

TYPE	SPAN	TOTAL WT.	EXPLOSIVE	SPEED	RANGE	MOTHER
I-GO "A"	6 M	1500 KG.	800 KG.	550 KM/HR	11 KM	Ki -67
I-GO "B"	4 M	750 KG.	300 KG	550 KM/HR	11 KM	Ki - 48

Japanese Heavy Bombers

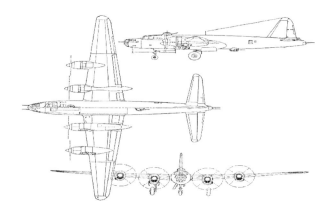

Nakajima G8N

Mitsubishi Ki-67

Nakajima G5N

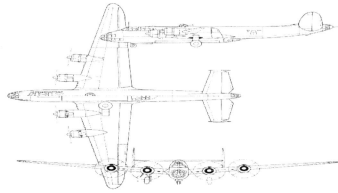

Nakajima G10N1

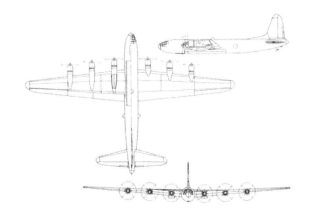

THE HEAT-HOMING BOMB

This type of bomb was planned for use solely against ships. They were to be employed at night because background conditions are more uniform for a heat-detector during that period. Nine different models were developed, but the first eight bombs were abandoned because of insufficient control. Mark IX, the latest, was designed with larger control surfaces, and it was expected that the final tests would be under way by the end of September 1945. It was stated that the Japanese obtained no outside aid in this development. Information was unsuccessfully sought from Germany. Two other applications of the heat-detector had been considered: heat-homing boats and aircraft installations to locate enemy planes. However, by far the greatest portion of the work was done on the heat-homing bomb. The heat-detector could detect a man's face at 100 metres (328 ft) and was therefore later given serious consideration for personnel detection.

Field Tests. The only model extensively produced and tested was the Mark VII. Fifty or 60 were dropped from a plane at 3000 metres (9843 ft altitude at a 10 x 20 metre (32,8 x 65.6 ft) raft target anchored near the centre of Lake Hamanako 2000 metres (6562 ft) in radius. The heat was provided by burning four 4x4 metre (13 x 13 ft) wood and coal fires on the surface of the raft. Less than 10 percent of the bombs reacted to the controls.

The Mark IX bomb. This final model was 5.45 metres (17.88 feet) long, 50 cm (19.7 ins) in diameter and weighed 800 kg (1764 lbs) (explosive charge was 200 to 300 kg (441 to 662 lbs). This model was provided with two sets of wings with aileron flaps controlled by an amplifier initiated by a bolometer in the nose of the bomb. Stabilisation was furnished by a gyroscope controlling four small flaps on the main wings. The speed was held back to 150 metres per second (492 fps) by a tail brake, in order to allow the controls time to operate. The controls were switched on automatically after descending to 2000 metres (6562 ft) altitude. From 2000 metres full control will change the point of impact by 600 metres (1968 ft) from the point of impact for free fall. A fuze was being designed to give an instantaneous burst with a direct hit on a ship, but providing delay on a water hit to give maximum damaging effect

THE ACOUSTIC FUZE

This device was planned solely for use in an anti 8-29 weapon. This fuze, sensitive to the Superfort's engine noise, was to be used in air-to-air bombing. In this manner Jap fighter-bombers could drop bombs into a .8-29 formation without considering altitude or fuze-setting and without necessitating direct hits.

Theoretical operation
The arming vane is jettisoned almost immediately. Ten seconds later (to allow the missile to clear the mother plane) the switches are closed, and the reception of the 8-29 noise causes a flow of current from the microphone. When the current reaches the desired flow, a relay is actuated, closing the switch of the fuze circuit and causing the bomb to explode.

Test and conclusions.
In laboratory bench tests, the sensitivity was of a good order and the action fairly accurate. However, in actual drop tests it was found that the microphone responded only to the background noises caused by the tail fins, and was insensitive to the engine signal. In cases of finless bombs the background noises were negligible, but the resulting erratic path of the bomb rendered it useless for operations.

Modifications in the microphone size, size of the microphone holes, alteration of fins etc were under consideration, but the Japanese scarcity of true high-altitude fighters slowed up the interest in the weapon. Finally, when (after the fall of Iwo Jima and Okinawa) the American fighter escort tactics began, the Japanese gave up the idea of overhead air-to-air bombing, and this fuze was abandoned before the end of the war.

Sonic-Controlled Bomb Fuse

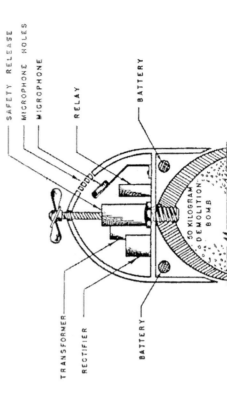

Fig GG

Heat Homing Bomb (Mk IX)

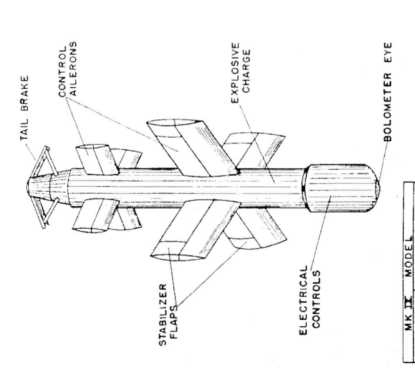

MK IX	MODEL
LENGTH	5.4 METERS
DIAMETER	50 CENTIMETERS
TOTAL WT.	800 KILOGRAMS
EXPLOSIVE	300 KILOGRAMS

Fig FF

Kawasaki Ki-66 Army Dive Bomber

15. AIRCRAFT ARMOUR

Rikugun Ki-93 Army Fighter

RESEARCH AND DEVELOPMENT

The first investigations of the practicability of using armour in aircraft were begun during the Sino-Japanese War, but serious efforts were not applied until 1939 when the Russo-Japanese border warfare was under way. At this time some of the Russian planes were found to be using armour sheet. The requirements for armour installations did not become urgent, however, until after the outbreak of the war with the United States.

Early in the conflict the Japanese studied the armour installations on the B-17 and at that time launched systematic investigations. These experiments were planned to develop the following:
- Special steels, especially ones using alloy substitutes for the critical nickel and molybdenum.
- Superior heat treatments.
- Composite armour sheet with double or triple layers arranged at various distances from each other (the optimum distance between two sheets of armour was stated to be two
- bullet lengths),
- New and improved methods of surface hardening
- Armour sheet to defeat explosive shells.

OPERATIONAL USE

In the early periods of the war, the Japanese used Ni-Cr-Mo, Mn-Cr-Mo, and Si-Mn-Cr steel for armour plate. Sheet thickness varied from two to 20 mm, but 8mm, 12mm and 16mm were finally adopted as standard. The 16mm was the most commonly used and would generally defeat all Allied armour-piercing and high-explosive projectiles.

The armour plate on a fighter weighed between 40 and 50 kg (88.2 and 110.25 lbs) and was generally installed behind the pilot. Bomber armour weighed up to 120 kg (234.6lbs) and was generally distributed between the pilot, co-pilot, and gunner.

Despite these satisfactory developments, some aircraft types were still designed without either armour or bullet-proof glass, and often with only one or the other. In many cases where armour was standard fighter equipment it was designed so as to be instantly detachable at the discretion of the pilot or organisation, and this procedure was common practice due to undesirable weight

COMPARISON WITH U.S. AIRCRAFT ARMOUR Chemical Analysis

Homogenous Steel aircraft armour

Japanese		United States Army	
Carbon	35-45	Carbon	34-45
Silicon	8-1.2	Chromium	1.10-1.30
Manganese	8-1.2	Molybdenum	50-70
Chromium	8-1.2	Vanadium	15-25
Same as homogenous except for		Carbon	12-18
Addition of carburised face.		Nickel	3.30-3.60
Surface hardening was incorporated		Molybdenum	25-35
In sheet thicknesses greater than 7mm		(90 carbon in case)	

PENETRATION TESTS

A comparison of United States and Japanese restivity rests for similar thicknesses of face-hardened place reveals negligible differences. Japanese requirements were slightly higher against A.P. penetration and slightly lower against H.E. shock.

Kawanishi H8K
Navy Flying Boat

Kawasaki H6K Flying Boat

16. RADAR EQUIPMENT

Tachikawa Ki-74 Army Reconnaissance aircraft

AIR-BORNE EQUIPMENT
Designs of operational Japanese airborne radar sets were somewhat similar to early American SCR-521. There were sea search, search and patrol (ASV - air to surface vessel), altimeter, and a few IFF sets in use; - but bombing through overcast (BTO) sets were still in the experimental stage when the war ended, A few aircraft interception (AI) sets had been. produced but it appears that they were not employed operationally. It seems, however, that some of the search sets were used in a limited manner for torpedo attacks, bombing, and for tracking large aircraft.

The Navy began study on carrier-borne radar late in 1941. From this research was developed the H-6 patrol and search set operating at 150 megacycles. About 2000 of these sets were produced by the Nihon Musen Co; and although they had limited accuracy their performance record was considered good. The lighter and more compact FK-3 was replacing the H-6 by the end of the war.

The Navy unsuccessfully tried adapting their 40 cm set No 22 to air-borne use to obtain greater accuracy in azimuth and range. In 1944, the Germans sent the Japanese completed schematics of their Rotterdam Gerat. A few sets were manufactured from these specifications but the distance at which it would pick up the shore was only 20 km (12.43. miles) which discouraged its large scale production.

In 1943, the Army produced its first airborne radar set. It was Taki 1, and was used in bombers for sea search. One Yagi antenna was mounted on the nose of the plane looking forward and a two x array was used on either side. Each of these antennas was capable of transmitting and receiving. By means of an antenna switch, all' three antennas could be. used in rapid rotation, or singly to determine relative direction by the maximum indication method on an A-type presentation tube. Electronic range markers provided accurate target ranging.

Taki 1 gave satisfactory search performance but its 330lbs was heavy for airborne equipment. A second Taki I was designed weighing only 176 lbs but it was still in the laboratory stage when the war ended. Both models operated on a frequency of 150 megacycles and were rated at 10 kw peak output power.. Their range against ships was 62 miles and against submarines 12.5 miles with an accuracy of plus or minus five degrees. A lighter model of Taki 1 had been developed for fighter bombers.

The Taki 2, which bears some resemblance to the German Lichtenstein (frequency and antenna) and the American SCR 540 (components) was being developed when the war ended. It was an 80-centimetre AI and ASV using Yugi arrays with folded dipoles. The transmitting antenna was installed on the nose of the plane with an antenna on each side of the nose for azimuth determination in addition to a vertically spaced pair for elevation. A motor driven distributor connected each receiving antenna to the receiver in rapid succession. There were three cathode ray tube display systems, with one scope for the pilot and two for the observers use. Of the two scopes utilised by the observers, one provided range (A type) and' the other indicated left-right and up-down signals. The remote cathode-ray tube used by the pilot duplicated this second presentation. A selsyn-controlled meter provided the pilot with the range of the target selected for viewing by the observer.

In late 1943, a 375-megacycle airborne surface search set, called Taki 3, was developed by Tokyo Imperial University. Two Vagi antennas were placed side by side on the' front of the plane to get direction. Fifty of these sets were produced but none ever were installed for operation because of its poor performance.

EARLY WARNING RADAR
The Japanese used a Doppler system of detection throughout the war in Japan and Korea. It was known as type A and' employed a radio transmitter operating on 40-80 megacycles which emitted continuous radio energy waves with superimposed audiO modulation in as narrow a beam as convenient to a receiving station from 40 to 100 miles away. When an aeroplane crossed the beam, the tone heard at the receiving station was interrupted and a heavy beat was picked up. The location of the body crossing the path of the transmission was unknown; the only thing known was that there was an object within a range of 100 miles from the transmitter and somewhere within the directive beam. Although It had the advantage in getting range with little power, it could not get a definite location. The longest type A line of detection used was from Formosa to Shanghai, a distance of over 400 miles.

In 1940, a Japanese technical commission returned from Germany with tales of advanced electronic development; and experimentation was begun in that year on pulsed radar, known as type B. Captured sets and data from the Phillipines and Malaya permitted the Japanese to produce type B units during 1942. The Army's Tachi 6, operating between 68-80 megacycles, proved too bulky for convenient use and two smaller more mobile sets were developed by June 1943. These were Tachi 7 and 18, both operating on 100 megacycles.

In 1942, the Army had built early warning radar sets designed for Army sea transport installation as they considered the Navy facilities unsatisfactory. After an unsuccessful attempt to set up their own sea air-warning system, the Army was forced to use these sets as fill-Ins for their land based radar warning system.

The Navy's first type B set, radio detector No 11 (Mark 1, model 1), also had been introduced in 1942 and also had been found too bulky,. By the end of the year, a smaller No 12 (Mark 1, model 11) had been built which was later adapted for ship-borne use. No 13 and 13K were likewise designed to effect simpler and lighter sets for naval use. In 1942, 10 cm ship-borne search sets were installed with magnetrons used in both the transmitters and receivers. Wave guides were used to pipe energy to the horn antennas. The range of these sets was only about 15.5 miles.

Radio detector NO 14 (mark 1, model IV) operating at 50 megacycles was designed and produced late in the war to provide greater protection against increasing B-29 attacks. Several sets were installed in southern Kyushu in 1945 with a stated range of about 186 miles.

GROUND CONTROL INTERCEPTION
The Japanese system of ground control interception was never satisfactory. A makeshift device was to employ two early warning sets, often Tachi 6 or 18, to track the enemy bombers and friendly interceptors respectively. There was no method of ascertaining the height of the enemy planes and. the bearing and range errors were so large that a final separation of 10 kilometres (6.2 miles) between the planes was the best that could be obtained.

Two proposed solutions to the GCI problem were being studied when the war ended. One was to use the IFF interrogator Tachi 13, transmitting at 184 megacycles and receiving at 175 megacycles, along the plane's transponder Taki 15 to both identify and fix the position of the night fighter. Another range finding radar would be employed to fix the position of the enemy plane at any moment..

The second system consisted of an automatic airborne transmitter, ground direction finding (D/F receivers and VHF (very high frequency) radio links from the direction-finding installations to the control centre. The airborne transmitter transmitted on a frequency of 190 megacycles per second and was modulated by any one of 30 pre-selected "identification" frequencies between 30 and 60 kilocycles per second. The transmitted signals were received by the ground direction-finding receivers, provided with lobe-switched antennas for greater accuracy. The antennas were rotated continuously at a speed of 2 revolutions per minute. The received signals at the three direction finding stations were related to the control centre over a VHF radio link operating in the frequency band from 50 to 65 megacycles. The control centre also was continuously supplied with information on the bearing of the direction finding antennas by the use of additional frequencies of 11, 13 and 15 kilocycles which modulated the very high frequency link..

At the control. centre, an azimuth "air-plot" picture was presented on a cathode ray tube, with an azimuth accuracy of one-halt percent. Assignment of each of the 30 available "identification" frequencies to selected aircraft permitted the control centre to track simultaneously a maximum of 30 planes by using the combined azimuth data from the three ground direction-finding receivers.

When the war ended, the Navy was developing radar sets for their new night fighters. ED-2 operating at 500 megacycles had a range of only 1.9 and 6.2 miles against other planes and ships respectively. It employed two sets of forward-looking Yagi antennas, one to transmit, the other to receive. Gyoku 3, operating at 150 megacycles had a range of 2.8 miles against medium type planes, but the set was never used operationally at night. It employed a specially constructed antenna which gave a forward looking conical scan. The antenna pattern was very broad, causing the image on the PPI (plan position indicator) tube to spread in azimuth with a resulting loss of definition.

GUN LAYING RADAR

Japanese gun-laying radar first appeared in 1943 and was patterned after captured British 5LC, GL Mark 11 and the American 5CR 268 sets. The complexity of the American unit made it difficult for the Japanese to copy, therefore their sets generally reflected the British influence. The first two army sets, Tach 1 and 2, had many features of the British 5LC unit. Tachi 1 had separately mounted receiving and transmitting antennas and Tachi 2 had both antennas on the same reflector framework; both sets operated on 200. megacycles. A phasing ring was used on both to give the receiver lobe generated by the four Yagi receiving antennas to a rotary movement. A mechanical distributor switched the received signal at appropriate moments to the azimuth or elevation scopes.

Tachi 4, which was developed to replace Tachi 1 and 2, was simplified by having transmitter and receiver mounted on the same carriage. This set was not very successful because it was inconvenient to handle and its accuracy was considered poor.
The Army favoured Tachi 3 of their gun-laying radar sets, which was styled after the British GL Mark ii and was operated at 78 megacycles, Its rated peak power output was 50 kilowatts. Pip-matching in both elevation and azimuth was accomplished by colour discs. The Navy had built a unit called 5-3 which was large and difficult to mass produce. It was replaced by the smaller, simpler, and more accurate 5-24. The Navy admitted that the Army's Tachi 3 had greater range compared to their equipment as azimuth elevation.

A modified Tachi 4, in production at the end of the war, was designed to operate on 200 megacycles and was to use the same four Vagi antennas for transmitting and receiving in order to provide greater range and azimith accuracy. The Army planned to adopt this set as their standard locator.

In early 1944, the complete plans of the small 570 megacycle German Wurzburg were received by submarine. Three modified copies built by Nippon Musen which were to be used as models by Sumitomo and Sibaura had been reproduced but were not operational when the war ended.

Kawanishi N1K1-J Shiden (George) Navy Fighter

17. PAPER BALOONS

DEVELOPMENT

This type balloon was originally used by the Japanese *for* weather forecasting. With this purpose in mind, research was carried on as early as 1935, with paper balloons having a diameter of 4 metres (13.1 ft) and capable *of* ascending to 6 km (3.73 miles) This objective having been attained studies ceased in 1935. When, on April 18 1942, Japan was first bombed (Doolittles's Raid) the effect on Japanese morale was such that all-out attempts were made to invoke retaliatory measures. Three methods *of* retaliation were under consideration by the Japanese General Staff; Balloons, aircraft and submarines. With the desire to strike at the American homeland, the paper balloon studies were revived and accelerated. The initial plan (1942) was to develop balloons capable of travelling a distance of 3000km (1864 miles) and which would be released from combat surface vessels or submarines *ott* the coast *of* the United States. This objective necessitated increasing the balloon diameter from 4 to 6 metres (13.1 to 19.7 ft) and then to 8 metres (26.2 ft). Finally, in 1943 the balloon design was increased to 10 metres (32.8 ft) in diameter, and by that summer it was thought that the balloon could travel th.e required 5000 km (1864 miles). However, the depleted Navy was so occupied by this time that ships were not available for carrying out the original plan of attack.

TRIAL LAUNCHINGS

In view of the general situation, new investigations soon got under way to construct a balloon capable of traversing the entire distance between Japan and the United States. By 11 February 1944, 200 10 metre (32.8 ft) diameter balloons were available for trial. All 200 were released on this date as a test. Only a few carried incendiaries; the majority carried sand only. A two station radio direction finder net, one station in Hokkaido and one in Chiba Prefecture, Honshu, was set up for this purpose of tracking the first part of the balloon's course. However, with this 250 mile base line, and as an admitted error of plus or minus two degrees, it was of course impossible to pin-point the location of balloons over 2000 miles away; especially, in view of the fact that no meteorological data was available to the Japanese for the vast distances involved. A knowledge of weather would have assisted them in projecting the probable route. Aside from the immediate vicinity of Japan, accurate information was limited to the western coast of the United States. America-n broadcasts were closely followed since there were no facilities for observing results. On an assessment of information received from their communications authorities regarding unexpected fires in the United States, it was felt that some damage had been done.

PRODUCTION AND MASS LAUNCHINGS

On the basis of these vague results, large-scale production of paper balloons began in April 1944. The cost Of each balloon was first close to 10,000 yen but later was somewhat reduced as production increased. These balloons were hand made and were farmed out to small factories. The desired objective in production was 20,000 balloons, but only about 9,000 were ever finished. All the balloons constructed were released. A small number of rubberised-silk balloons carried radio transmitter (1000 mile range) and gave additional assistance in plotting the balloon's course. Although the first specimens of the mass production were available in July and August, none was released until 20 November 1944. From then on, as many balloons as possible were sent in the direction of the United States, depending only upon production and. existing meteorological conditions. The largest number of balloons ever sent in one month, 3,000 were released in March 1945, although climatic conditions were not most favourable during that month. On 13 March 1945, 2 balloons were returned, after a 24 hour trip, to Japanese shores by freak winds. These were the only balloons to turn back and they did no damage since they fell in snowbanks. The last group of balloons was released on 20 April 1945.

BOMB LOAD

The balloon payload was invariably two-thirds incendiary and one third high explosive. and it was apparently never intended to alter these loads with chemical warfare materials or other weapons. The maximum bomb capacity estimated for each balloon by the. Japanese was 30kg (66lbs); the average load was 24 kg (53lbs), and the lightest was 12 kg (26.41bs).

OBJECTIVES AND RESULTS

The objective for this weapon was solely retaliation, and the Japanese did not expect it to be very effective. They stated that they would have been entirely satisfied if one third of these balloons reached the United States. It is apparent that the ascent of the balloons was accompanied by much propaganda effort to uplift home front morale and to stimulate general production efforts. However, Japanese military officials stated that if the war continued, the materials used for balloon production were to be given to other industries.

Paper Balloon Bombs

TYPE 92
15 KILOGRAM
HE BOMB

TYPE 100 5 KG
INCENDIARY

TYPE 97 12 KG
INCENDIARY

METAL POSTS

BAKELITE PLATE

ALUMINUM RING

DEMOLITION CHARGE

DIRECTION OF BURN
2 MIN 45 SEC

WIRED TO NO. 6 C.P.
ON BAKELITE PLATE

WIRED TO MASTER
LEAD

1½ V WET-CELL BATTERY

SUSPENSION BRIDLE

ANEROIDS IN BOX

TWO SOFT FUSES
FOR EACH DROP
ACTION, BURNING
56 SEC EA MIN

FUSE TO BALLOON
FLASH BOMB

WIRED TO FIREBOMB
ON OTHER WING

WIRED TO NO. 6 C.P.
ON BAKELITE PLATE

SAND BALLAST

CENTER MAIN
BOMB RELEASE

ALUMINUM RING

SINGLE RELEASE UNIT

ONE "T" BAR TWO BLOWOUT PLUGS

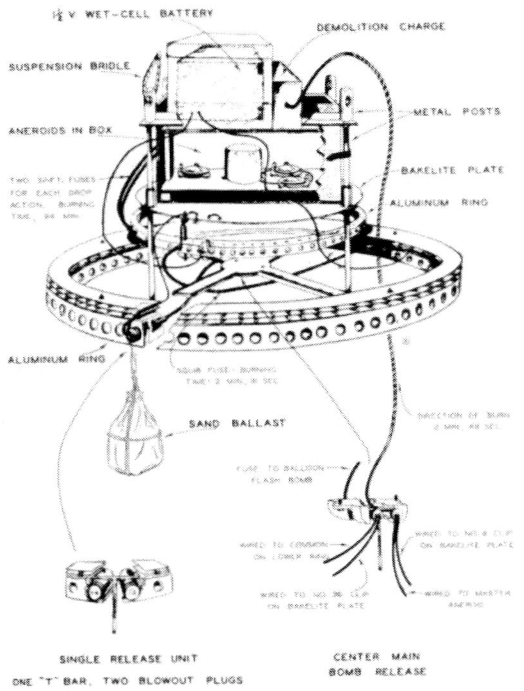

Automatic altitude-control device

Japanese Paper Balloons

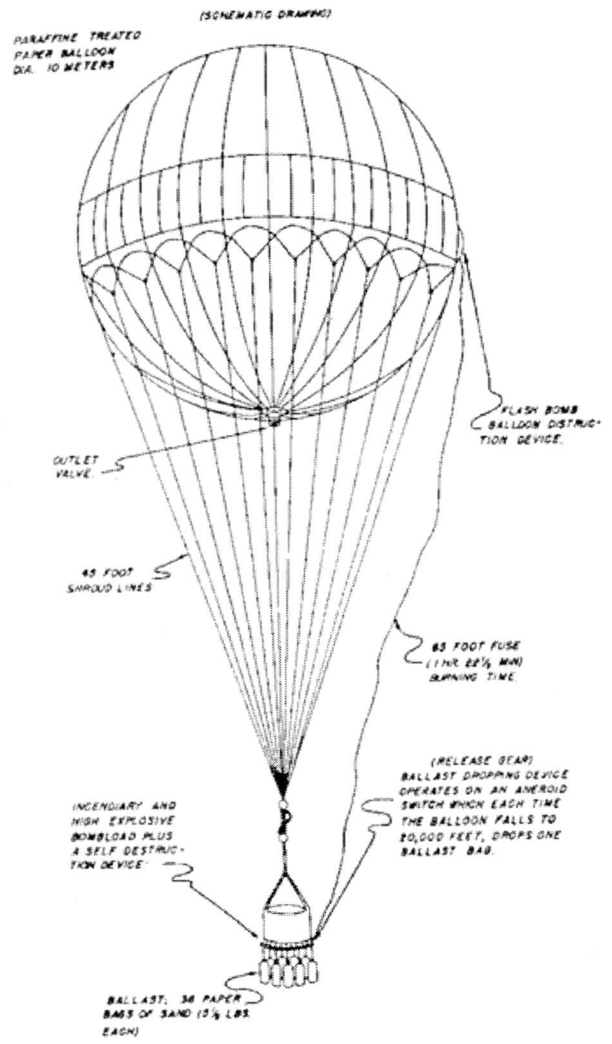

(SCHEMATIC DRAWING)

PARAFFINE TREATED
PAPER BALLOON
DIA. 10 METERS

FLASH BOMB
BALLOON DESTRUC-
TION DEVICE

83 FOOT FUSE
(1 HR 22½ MIN)
BURNING TIME

(RELEASE GEAR)
BALLAST DROPPING DEVICE
OPERATES ON AN ANEROID
SWITCH WHICH EACH TIME
THE BALLOON FALLS TO
30,000 FEET, DROPS ONE
BALLAST BAG

OUTLET
VALVE

45 FOOT
SHROUD LINES

INCENDIARY AND
HIGH EXPLOSIVE
BOMBS(D) PLUS
A SELF DESTRUC-
TION DEVICE

BALLAST, 36 PAPER
BAGS OF SAND (15½ LBS.
EACH)

85.

Fig HH

On 4 November 1944, a rubberised-silk balloon, supporting electronic devices, was retrieved from the ocean off the coast near San Pedro, California. Ten days later' a paper balloon was picked up in the ocean near Hawaii. By 28 August 1945, a total of 296 confirmed balloon incidents were reported (including three of the rubberised type). These incidents ranged from Alaska to Mexico, and included the Aleutian Islands, 5 Canadian provinces, and 17 States in the western USA. Existing American radar equipment could not give satisfactory results in identification or detection of these balloons due to the weakness of the signal involved.
The American press furnished the Japanese with their best source of information by reporting the landing places of several balloons. This data touched off the Japanese propaganda programme on 17 February 1945 when reference was made to the balloons in a Domei broadcast to the United States. The Japanese claimed that 500 casualties had been inflicted in the United States and numerous fires started. The broadcast also announced the United States authorities had found it necessary to issue general warnings against attacks by the Japanese balloons and thus had aggravated unrest among the people. It was emphasised that these occurrences had shattered the American feeling of security against attacks by the Japanese.

Subsequently Japanese broadcasts beamed to Europe, south east Asia, arid China repeated this theme, and in one instance, added that several million airborne troops could be landed in the United States in the near future.

A broadcast in English from Singapore (Nappo-Domei) on 4 June 1945 predicted that when the "experimental" period is past, "large-scale attacks with death-defying Japanese airmen manning the balloons will be launched". A further inference of possible impending activity was made by the manager of the Domei news agency in Argentina who later stated that the balloons were a "prelude to something big".

It was realised in the United States that one evident purpose of the paper balloons was the transportation of incendiary and anti-personnel bombs. Military intelligence reactions pointed to the possible further utilisation of the balloons as a prelude to the following activities, all of which were deemed practicable:

- Biological warfare.
- Transportation of agents
- Wind current data for long-range bomber attacks.

CONCLUSION
In view of the Japanese home front propaganda effect, and in consideration of the geographical location of the balloon landings, the paper balloon campaign was not an unsuccessful enterprise. In evaluating the 296 witnessed incidents, it must be realised that undoubtedly some balloons had arrived which were totally destroyed by the proper functioning of the incorporated destruction devices. The payload was principally incendiary, and a plotting of bomb incidents and balloon recoveries show that the great majority landed in the heavily forested areas of western United States, Canada and Alaska. .

Kawasaki Ki-61 Hien (Tony) Army Fighter

PRODUCTION OF MAIN TYPES

Fighters

A6M (Zero)	20,898
Ki-43 (Oscar)	5919
Ki-84 (Frank)	3514
Ki-61 (Tony)	3078
N1K1 (George)	1435
Ki-44 (Tojo)	1225
J2M (Jack)	476

Bombers

G4M (Betty)	2446
Ki-21 (Sally)	2064
P1Y (Frances)	1098
G3M (Nell)	1048
Ki-49 (Helen)	819
Ki-67 (Peggy)	698

Naval Attack

D4Y-3 (Judy)	2038
B6N (Jill)	1268
B7A (Grace)	114

Dive Bombers

Ki-5 (Nick)	1701
D3Y (Val)	1495

Reconnaissance

Ki-46 (Dinah)	1742
C6N (Myrt)	463

Flying Boats

H6K (Mavis)	215
H8K (Emily)	167

18. DEATH RAY

GENERAL
The Japanese worked on a "death ray" for *five* and a half years. The apparatus was based on the principle that very short radio waves focussed in a beam of high power will cause physological effects in mammals, resulting in death. The principle purpose of the research was to develop a military weapon which would cause paralysis or death to any human being upon whom the beam was focussed. The primary application was expected to be as an anti aircraft device since the equipment was not easily portable.

Throughout this programme experiments were also tried on the effectiveness of short-wave radiation in stopping engines by causing pre-ignition.

The research was thought promising enough to invest two million yen on it, though it never reached the stage of practical application. Research was eventually placed in direct charge of General Kusaba whose section had earlier done the work on the paper balloons.

RESEARCH PROGRAMME

Effects against living things:

1940: Studies were initiated with the observation of injurious effects to mice and ground hogs in the field between condenser plates.
1941: A further study on the ellipsoidal focus was carried out.
1942. The causes and effects were studied physiologically and pathologically
1943: Studies revealed that waves from 2 metres (78.74 ins) to 60 cm (22.62 ins) in length caused haemorrhage of lungs; waves shorter than 2 metres (78.74 ins) destroyed brain cells.
1944. More extensive studies were begun of the radiating electric field at a distance of 10 to 30 metres (32.8 to 98.4 ft) from the apparatus.
1945, Investigations ceased due to termination of the war.

Effects against engines.
1942 Studies were initiated with experiments on stopping automobile engines.
1943. It was found possible to stop engines (unless completely shielded) by tuned waves.
1944; Studies against aircraft engines were unsuccessful due to good shielding.
1945: Investigation began as to the effect of the waves in passing through the gap of
The engine cover.

EXPERIMENTS ON ANIMALS
The general nature of the apparatus was a high power short-wave oscillator feeding a dipole antenna which was placed at the focus of an ellipsoidal reflector. The animal was placed at the other focus of the ellipsoid. Experiments were conducted on mice, rabbits, ground hogs and monkeys.
In 1944, with the 80 centimetre, 30 kilowatt magnetron feeding a dipole in a one metre reflector, rabbits were killed in ten minutes at a distance of 30 metres (98.4 ft); ground hogs took 20 minutes. No monkeys were utilised in these later experiments due to difficulties in obtaining specimens during the war.
The experiments planned in 1945 were to use four 300 watt (input) magnetrons in parallel which were expected to give a total output .of 250 to 300 kilowatts. These were to feed a dipole in a 10 metre (32.8 ft) diameter ellipsoidal reflector. It was calculated that this apparatus would kill a rabbit in 10 minutes at a distance of 1 km (.62 mile) Wave lengths shorter than 80 cm (31.5 ins) appeared to be more effective, but research was concentrated on 80 cm (31.5 ins) because this was the shortest wave length which the Japanese knew how to build output oscillators. .

FUTURE POTENTIALITIES
Allied research on radar has resulted in the development of higher power and shorter wavelength oscillators. If the Japanese experiments are reliable indications of the potentialities of the death ray, it is considered within the realm of possibility by eminent Allied scientists that a ray apparatus might be developed, that could kill unshielded human beings at a distance of 5 to 10 miles.